The Healing Powers of
Chromotherapy

The Author Before and After

Before

After

The Healing Powers of
Chromotherapy

using colours to cure diseases

Hari Om Gupta

A Sterling Paperback

STERLING PAPERBACKS
An imprint of
Sterling Publishers (P) Ltd.
A-59, Okhla Industrial Area, Phase-II,
New Delhi-110020.
Tel: 26387070, 26386209; Fax: 91-11-26383788
E-mail: sterlingpublishers@airtelmail.in
ghai@nde.vsnl.net.in
www.sterlingpublishers.com

The Healing Powers of Chromotherapy
© 2007, Hari Om Gupta
ISBN 978-81-207-3253-7
Reprint 2008

Printed and Published by Sterling Publishers Pvt. Ltd.,
New Delhi-110 020.

CONTENTS

FOREWORD

Sh. Hari Om Gupta is working as a social worker in the city of Ludhiana in the domain of medicine and his cherished field is chromotherapy. He is a great industrialist but at present his real wealth is his dedication to the service of the poorest of the poor. He is a close friend of mine and because of his lovable personality his colleagues call him, *Gupta Sahib.*

In the beginning he started the treatment of the patients at his residence free of cost with the help of water, sugar crystals, honey, Vaseline, *desi ghee,* sun-charged oil and the results were astonishing. People began to approach him in large numbers and those who were given the treatment were mostly benefitted. Now he thinks it is his humble duty to serve the ailing humanity.

He has written many books, one after another, on the subject of chromotherapy. He has written other books like *Old Age, Health and Beauty, Constipation, Asthma, Relief from Skin Diseases, Heart Diseases, Blood Pressure, Depression and Sleeplessness, Cure from Cancer* and *Say Good Bye to Temperature,* etc. These books are in great demand in the market because of their usefulness. His books, on the subject of health care, *yogasana* and *pranayama* are full of bundles of wisdom and those who will study and practise them will definitely lead a healthy and enjoyable life.

We should all come forward to do whatever we can to help the suffering humanity so that this world can become a better place to live in.

Ved Parkash Khara (M.A., M.Ed.), P.E.S. (Retd.)
Acting President Sr. Citizens Assn., Nehru Rose Garden,
Ludhiana

FOREWORD

A living being gets the energy to live from the Sun God. This energy is vital to keep one healthy. The human body is made up of five elements as mentioned by Saint Tulsidas i.e., *chhat, jal, pawak, gaman, sameera*. These five elements get their life-energy from the Sun God.

A living being gets the energy to live from the Sun God. This energy is vital to keep one healthy. The human body is made up of five elements as mentioned by Saint Tulsidas i.e. *chhat, jal, pawak, gaman, sameera*. These five get their life-energy from the Sun God.

The rays of the sun are mainly of seven types and these seven rays are called the seven horses of the Sun God. Every ray has a different colour and a different chemical is required to prepare a colour. The human body also has seven power points. Every point has a different colour, use and look. A change in the proportion of a chemical affects the colour thus disturbing the balance. This disturbance in balance is the main cause of all illnesses.

The morning and the evening rays of the sun are extremely helpful in curing illnesses. Our saints and teachers have explored this truth deeply through meditation and on practical basis and have explained it completely in our *Vedas* and *Shastras*.

A deep study has been made in India and abroad on this subject and many books have been written on it. They have explained the waves of different colours of the sun rays and their velocity.

Nature cure can keep a person healthy. Great saints, ayurvedic doctors and doctors practising nature cure have done a great service to the humanity by writing extensively on the topic. They have excelled in this field because they practise the therapy selflessly.

Today we find human beings to be the sickest living beings on earth. Other living beings that come in contact with human beings also tend to fall ill.

Sun has the power to cure all our ailments. Even cancer can be cured by the sunrays. Sun-bathing gives strength, energy, courage and speed to our body. Even our *Shashtras* have laid emphasis on having sun-bath for at least 10-15 minutes. It is for this reason that when water is offered to Sun God after bathing the rays of the sun get refracted by water and reach our body and keep us healthy. These sunrays have mineral elements.

Mr Gupta has made an attempt to give us the free and effective ways of curing even serious illnesses.

Natural Therapy Trust
Ludhiana

PREFACE

I was so engulfed by sickness that I had almost decided upon committing suicide. One day I decided that I had enough and started for Haridwar. Instead of Haridwar I went to Rishikesh. I was suffering from migraine, diabetes that also at its highest level, boils had emerged on my back and head and pus had started coming out of my legs. Because of diabetes the skin on my hands had begun to peel off. In the morning on waking up I would find my fingers stiff because of pain. It would take me 15-20 minutes to get rid of the stiffness. Walking and climbing up the stairs had become difficult. I had to clutch my knee joints at every step.

I cannot describe the other ailments I suffered due to diabetes — blood pressure, weakness, insomnia which made me stay awake all night and the sleep I got during the day was insignificant. As a result I suffered from stress. So much so that my hands lost the power to hold. This condition forced me to take about 12 tablets from morning to night and I was always worried of missing a dose or not having enough of medicine. At times I used to overdose myself.

I started staying at Vanprastha Ashram in Rishikesh. After a few days I met a gentleman. One day while chatting with him I happened to tell him about my problem of insomnia and my worry regarding it. The gentleman said that my problem was not a big deal. He asked me to bring a small bottle and come to his room. I did so. Then by giving me 10-12 drops of an oil he asked me to massage it on my forehead, temple, centre of the head with my fingers at night before going to sleep without taking my sleeping pills. He said that I would sleep soundly and that's exactly what happened.

When I woke up in the morning I felt very light. My mind was joyous. I did the same thing the next night again without taking my sleeping pills and I slept soundly.

On the 3rd day when I woke up my body was full of energy and I was very happy. I wondered about the magic that oil contained that had acted so fast. I spent the whole day wondering. In the evening when I took the empty bottle to the gentleman's room and asked him for some more drops he politely refused explaining that he needed the oil for himself. He told me that every person who had used the oil had been benefited and had called it magic oil. He further told me that one of his friends who stayed in Chandigarh prepared medicine using sunrays. He showed me some other bottles containing other medicines. It was not his business. He was actually a big officer. The gentleman then gave me a book to read, as promised. I spent another week there and came back home. I ordered for the book from Delhi and got its delivery within 10 days. The author of the book was Dr. Dwarkanath Narang.

After reading the book I started doing self-medication, preparing medicines, consuming them and followed the instructions dutifully. I was fully fit within three months. Earlier my weight was 97 kgs, but after the cure it came down to 70. I was completely fit. I got rid of all my pills. All my ailments had disappeared. I started going for morning walk for 8-10 kilometers. People started asking me the magic behind it. Today I cure people using the various techniques of chromotherapy for free. I have started *Aashirwad Surya Kiran Chikitsa and Rang Chikitsa Kendra* – a centre that provides free treatment.

In this book I have mentioned those methods of self cure that are cost-free, investment free, easy to understand, health-oriented and a valuable gift of nature. After deeply understanding the principles of this branch of science, I have written this book.

Anyone with an intention to serve mankind can understand this great gift of nature and can be helpful in popularising this knowledge. One can use this knowledge for self-cure. No specific place is required for this purpose.

I am greatly thankful to those saints and preachers who have kept this knowledge safe and to those who have published it. I request you not to follow the techniques given in this book blindly but under the guidance of a trained therapist. Taking the help of the book written by Dr. Dwarkanath Narang, and testing it with successful results on thousands of patients, I have shared my knowledge with you in this book.

Hari Om Gupta

INTRODUCTION

*C*hromotherapy is one of the oldest healing systems and it exists in every part of the world. For thousands of years this traditional non-chemical drug therapy was unknown to the whole world. But the recent popularity of alternative therapies among different communities of the world reflects the need to rely on natural, safe and time-tested methods of treatment. It is not only popular in India but also in other countries like America, Japan, etc. Chromotherapy combines the benefits of sun and the colours to cure various ailments.

Sunrays possess therapeutic powers that are beneficial to one's health, both physical and mental. Growth and development of one's body is dependent on sunlight which consists of energy and colour. A single ray of sunshine encompasses all the colours of the spectrum. Our bodies select from the sunlight whatever colours are needed for maintaining the correct balance, the corresponding or respective vibrations being absorbed into us.

Chromotherapy is a discipline that aims-to harness solar energy in order to treat various ailments. Numerous experiments have been conducted to prove that the closer a therapeutic system is to nature, the more powerful and influential it is. Where there is sunlight, there is energy and colour, and hence sunrays form the basis of chromotherapy.

Seven colours are emitted by the sun. These seven colours of the sunrays have therapeutic qualities. The rays of any colour can be absorbed by the body with the help of a coloured glass. Our body has self-healing powers which can cure diseases and make us healthy and chromotherapy boosts this self-healing ability.

CHROMOTHERAPY

History of Chromotherapy

Sun is the source of life on earth. From the beginning of the human civilisation sun has been worshipped as the giver of life and power. Making obeisance to the sun early in the morning helps to purify and harmonise the functioning of the various organs in the body. Among all other methods for treatment of various diseases, treatment through solar energy always held a special place.

In the Vedas sun has been called the soul of mother nature. It has been mentioned in Rig Veda, Yajur Veda and Atharva Veda. Even in the *Prashnopanishad* sun has been called the life of a human being and it is believed that for a healthy body one has to take the shelter of the sun. It is for this reason that the *rishis* of the olden times had started a ritual of *surya namaskar* and *surya upasana*. The Vedas have made a strong mention of the rising sun. In a mantra of Atharva Veda it has been said that the rays of a rising sun eliminate all the causes of ailments. A rising sun emits rays of red colour. These red rays have life energy and the power to destroy ailments. In the Rig Veda it has been said that the rays of a rising sun can cure all heart problems, jaundice, deficiency of blood, etc.

In this regard the 18th chapter of the 9th section of Atharva Veda is specially important. It has a long list of 22 *mantras* that tell us about those ailments curable through sunrays. The ailments mainly mentioned are – headache, pain in the ear, blindness, bodyache, stiffness, all types of fever, dropsy, swollen body, different ailments of the stomach, effects of poison, infections, heart problems, urinary problem, lung diseases, intestinal and sexual ailments, joint pain, etc. According to Rig Veda, sun provides human beings health, long life and happiness. In one mantra it has been said that sunrays save a human being from death.

It is an old story. One day Gemni muni was sitting under a tree in his *ashram*. On one branch of the tree a bird suddenly said "KOORUKOO" which means –"Who is healthy?" Gemni muni understood the language of the birds and said, "HIT BHU KU", which means, "One who consumes beneficial, best and nourishing food". The bird again said, "KOORUKOO". Then the muni again replied, "MITH BHUKOO" i.e. "the person who consumes an appropriate amount of food." The bird again said, "KOORUKOO". Then the muni again replied, "HITBHUKOO AND MITH BHUKOO", which means, "only that person can enjoy his body who takes his meals according to his nature and in appropriate quantity at a fixed time. Only he can have a happy and long life."

In ancient times various methods were used to cure ailments but chromotherapy held a special place. Different types of ailments were cured by the sunrays. Wells used to be broad so that the rays of the sun and the moon could reach the water.

In the western society this therapy was popularised by General Palinjan Honey. After him American doctors, Dr. S. Pancost and Dr. Robert Bohland and an English doctor Edwin Babbitt further popularised this therapy. Slowly this knowledge spread to France and the rest of Europe. Now enough literature is available on this therapy.

In India this therapy has spread in limits. The responsibility for writing literature on this topic mainly goes to Shri Gobind Bapu Tongu and Dr. Dwarkanath Narang. Now many books are available in Hindi on this subject.

The Teachings of Acharya Charak
Maharishi Charak is the supreme of Ayurveda. He had great knowledge of all the *shastras* and he has explained in detail the benefits of sunrays. In his preachings he has stated that the root cause of all ailments is misfortune and the other name of misfortune is desire. Desire leads to sorrows. So lack of desire leads to the end of sorrow.

3

According to him *yog* and *moksh* end all sufferings. Moksh ends sufferings and yog leads to moksh. Acharya Charak has also stressed on keeping the body healthy and has said that with health one gets strength, age and great happiness. It also provides infinite fruits.

Maharishi Charak has said that whenever a physician encounters an ailment about which he has no knowledge, he should not accept defeat because of the lack of knowledge about it. Ayurveda claims that though ailments are infinite, their cure is short and well-scheduled. So every ailment can be fought against and won. So no physician should be frightened of an unknown ailment and accept defeat at its hands instead of fighting with it.

The Reasons of Ailments

All ailments take place due to wind, phlegm and bile.

1. *Bile* : In ailments caused due to bile, the heat in the body increases.
2. *Phlegm* : Ailments due to phlegm are caused by increase in coldness in the body.
3. *Wind* : The main reason of wind ailments is the collection of dirt and waste materials in the body.

Both the doctor and patient should understand this clearly that except for accidents and epidemics all ailments are curable but they should be cured with proper understanding. All the ailments are mainly caused due to the accumulation of injurious enzymes and poisonous elements.

These polluted elements get collected in the body because of wrong diet and life style.

The body tries to cure itself with its life energy by removing this dirt from the body with great hard work. All ailments such as cold, loose motions, fever, etc., are the processes of the body to remove all the dirt and poison accumulated inside it. This life energy should be provided the support of chromotherapy. This eliminates the ailment from its root.

Principles of Chromotherapy

Wrong lifestyle, improper diet, stress, tension, fear, anger, worry, lack of exercise, consumption of harmful products like liquor, cigarette, etc., are some of the causes for the many illnesses people are engrossed with these days. It is a tough job to keep a body healthy at all ages and in all seasons because a body is a temple of problems and a house of ailments. Due to ailments one has to take medical help.

Chromotherapy is the most natural of all treatments. It combines the benefits of sun and colours to treat various diseases. Sun gives us energy and colour, therefore sun forms the basis of chromotherapy. Sunrays have healing powers and in conjunction with medicines, water, colour, gems, etc., they are even more effective. Chromotherapy is a discipline that aims to harness the solar energy in order to treat various ailments of the body. According to chromotherapy the human body absorbs the sunrays through the skin which effects the endocrine glands, blood cells and the chemical reactions of the body. The colourful light stimulates and oxidises the body, thus restoring the balance of the body.

This therapy makes use of the seven visible rays of the sun for the treatment of diseases. Seven colours are emitted by the sun. These seven colours have therapeutic qualities.

Different types of mediums are used in the treatment like water, *mishri*, pure *ghee* of cow's milk, coloured bottles, rose water, honey, etc. Solarisation produces medicinal properties in these substances which are then effective in curing various ailments.

Benefits of Chromotherapy

Solar power, a natural source of light and energy, is available free of cost and in abundance. Sunlight converts the inactive Vitamin D in our bodies to its active form, which is essential for healthy bones. Solarised water, sugar, oil, etc., are effective in curing ailments. Sunrays are useful in correcting the deficiency or excess of a particular chemical in any part of the body. Sun is also a good source for pigmentation of one's skin. The early rays of sun are beneficial in activating the pituitary gland. The flora and fauna get their life from the sun. We get many important elements from sunrays which are required for the growth of the body. Sunrays eliminate pain and also strengthen our bones.

Solarised water contains calcium which gives strength to the body. Solarised blue or violet colour is helpful in baldness and greying of hair. Sun-charged green oil is beneficial in skin problems. Solarised yellow or orange water is useful in cleaning the bowels and curing spleen related problems. Chromotherapy helps to balance the frequencies of malfunctioning cells and to bounce back to our natural state of radiant well-being. We get energy and colour from sunrays. Various parts of the body as well as the organs are affected by different colours. Colours can be enormously helpful not only therapeutically, but also in such fields as meditation, tarot reading, distance healing, crystal-gazing, clairvoyance, mirror-gazing, etc. The red end of the spectrum stimulates, while blue end calms, as it has a cooling and soothing effect. Colour is everything for colour is all what we are made of. Symbolising season, direction, rank and royalty, colour is a vital healing force. Apart from other diseases chromotherapy has been proved to cure even cases of addiction.

Surya Namaskar, supplemented with yoga, enables the body to be united with the mind, the matter with the spirit, and the physical with the spiritual. By regularly practising yoga one can achieve purity, contentment, self-awareness, and the will to surrender to the will of God. All the organs and systems in the body get rejuvenated, thus complementing the beneficial effects of chromotherapy.

Usually colours are chosen and used for the purpose of beauty but when this therapy is used as a science these colours are used for curative purposes. For making proper use of these colours and making the body healthy in an efficient and effective manner it is necessary to practise chromotherapy. The endocrine system of our body reacts to different colours. This therapy doesn't have any side effects. There is no need of surgery or anaesthesia and is totally painless.

HEALING WITH COLOURS

$\mathcal{T}$he principle underlying the concept of healing with colours is to give the body an added dose of any colour that is lacking. The various parts of the body as well as the organs are affected by different colours. Chromotherapy helps in restoring the colour and the chemical balance. Sunlight, colour and heat affect the development and growth of the body in several ways. Seven colours are emitted by the sun. Of these seven colours – violet, indigo, blue, green, yellow, orange and red– only red, yellow and blue are primary colours. The others are secondary and tertiary colours, which are combinations of these primary colours. These seven colours of the sunrays have therapeutic qualities. These are divided into three groups, namely – red, orange and yellow; green; blue, indigo and violet. It is from these groups that the therapist needs to choose only one group for treatment.

Power of Colours

Red

Red symbolises love and procreation, but is also associated with violence and death. It symbolises and stimulates passion.

Orange

Orange is associated with the symbol of wisdom, intuition, spontaneity, and living in the present moment. It represents health, mind, and great ambitions.

Yellow

Yellow represents intelligence, wisdom and loyalty. Yellow has been associated with the divine symbols of creation since time immemorial.

Green
Green symbolises peace and prosperity.

Blue
Blue symbolises trust, peace, contentment, optimism, etc. All Hindus, Buddhists, native Americans and Chinese associate blue with the heavens.

White
White is associated with truth, purity. For Hindus white is the symbol of self- illumination.

Violet
Violet represents faith, power and modesty.

Use of Colours in the Treatment of Diseases
In ancient Rome one therapy which was extremely famous was 'Helio therapy'. In Roman 'Helio' means sun, so it is the sun therapy. Similarly there is a therapy called chromotherapy where *chromo* means colour. This therapy combines the benefits of the sun as well as the benefits of the various colours of the sun to cure different ailments of the body. In ancient Rome there were solariums at various places where chromotherapy was practised and the patients got free treatment. In the city of Rome there were dispensaries of 'Chromo Hydropathy'. Here too, ailments were treated using chromotherapy.

During rainy season, the clean rain water or water in the well used to be filled in seven different coloured bottles and their mouth covered with sticky mud. After this the bottles were kept in a solarium at a place where the sunrays would fall. In this way by keeping the coloured bottles in the sun for 3-4 days the water in those bottles would become life-saving. It obtains the power to cure ailments.

1. *Blue*
Blue is very powerful in destroying ailments due to bile. Oranges, lemon, chloroform, sapphire, etc., have the elements of blue in them. The water of a blue bottle gives coolness, quenches thirst, stops internal and external bleeding and reduces fever.

The massage of sun-charged blue oil is a tonic for those who do mental work. It is beneficial in headache, fever, loose motions with bleeding, acne, insomnia, piles, etc. Some people call this sun-charged blue oil a miracle.

This blue oil is beneficial in insect bites, stings, etc., and if there is pain in the ear this oil can be put in the ear after heating it a little. If one is suffering from throat infections due to heat then one should gargle with blue water and blue sun-charged glycerine should be applied. If the gums and/or teeth are swollen then blue glycerine is useful.

2. Green

This colour helps to get rid of infectious ailments and gives strength. Amla, green vegetables, etc., have the elements of green colour in them. The greatest quality of the colour green is that it provides strength to those parts of our body that remove foreign matter.

The sun-charged green water is highly useful in typhoid, eczema, etc. Infectious ailments like septic, leucorrhoea, constipation, etc., can be eliminated using this water.

This solarised green water is beneficial for stomach and intestinal ulcers. Every ailment of the eye can be cured by washing or applying a few drops of this sun-charged green water into the eyes.

3. Red

This colour provides strength and heals all the ailments of cough. There is a huge treasure of red rays in raw mangoes, honey, garlic, iron, aromatic seeds, etc. Red colour is very hot in nature so it should be used only for external purpose. A massage of sun-charged red oil is most beneficial.

4. Orange

Orange water increases hunger, helps in digestion, increases strength and is effective in relieving flatulence. Orange water helps to increase the red blood corpuscles in the body. It acts as a tonic for aged people. It gives relief in problems like vomiting, fear, stomachache and bed-wetting in children. This water provides relief in loose motions and gastritis. Drinking orange water in paralysis is highly beneficial.

Exposing the affected area to red light and massaging it with sun-charged red oil is highly beneficial.

Drinking orange water helps in relieving menstrual pain. In cold, cough, asthma, pneumonia, etc., massaging the chest with sun-charged red oil or radiation of red light is highly beneficial.

For joint pain, pain in the knee, waist, neck the *Aashirwad Mahanarayni oil's* massage gives quick results.

If the ear is filled with pus or there is deafness then 3-4 drops of sun-charged red oil should be warmed and dropped into the ear or the ear can be exposed to red light for beneficial results. The sun-charged red oil is massaged on the effective part of a T.B. patient or if the red light is radiated on it then it has a relaxing effect.

5. *White*

It has equal amount of blue, red and green colour. The water prepared with it is free from germs and it can be drunk as per the thirst. It has no side effects and it acts as a tonic for children. It can be drunk in place of plain water. Because it has calcium in it, it provides strength to children and helps in teething.

Note: *In the above given uses the sun-charged orange water, sun-charged red water, sun-charged green water and sun-charged red oil mean that the given water or oil has been solarised by being exposed to the sunrays. So orange water should not be considered as orange juice.*

Deficiency of Colours

According to chromotherapy it is the imbalance of colours that causes all ailments. We can see the deficiency of an element in the body in a definite, easy and economical way by looking at the colour of the affected organ of the body. By looking at a yellow face we can easily conclude that it is due to the deficiency of yellow colour in the body or weakness. By looking at yellow coloured eyes we can conclude that it is due to jaundice.

The colour of cough, urine, stool and other excreta show the problems the body contains. If it were not the question of colour then why would you be worried at the colour of urine being too yellow or red. You realise that you are sick if your tongue starts turning white or your nails yellow. If the tongue becomes bluish black then it signals death.

Surely the presence of various colours in the body needs to be all right. If the natural colour of a body part increases or decreases then it is a symptom of an ailment. The physicians of chromotherapy try to balance this colour deficiency by providing different colours to the affected body part. For example, lack of green colour causes burning sensation and dryness in the eyes, nails, yellowness of the skin, liquid or thin faeces, excess cold, excess anger, dysentery, jaundice, etc. Lack of red colour causes excessive sleepiness, laziness, constipation, etc.

The practitioner listens to all the problems of the patient and looks at the affected areas, assesses the situation and then decides upon the cure. For deciding upon the treatment the physician requires a good sense of judgement. Every body part has a different ailment and so a different cure. If the ailments are different then they have to be cured in different ways. Every part of our body requires different colours of light.

Chemical Elements in the Body and Colours

There are different chemical elements present in various kinds of foods. The body gets elements like magnesium, potassium, sodium, silicon, calcium, lithium, copper, iron, phosphorus, sulphur, mercury, etc., through the consumption of various kinds of foods.

Doctors by experiment have found different chemicals in the sunrays:

1. *Violet, Indigo and Blue* – The rays of these colours are found to have calcium, aluminium and hydrogen.

2. *Green* – Green is quite rich and abundant in oxygen, aluminium, chromium, sodium, calcium, nickel, carbon, nitrogen and other such elements.

3. *Yellow, Orange and Red* – Calcium, magnesium, nitrogen, barium, iron, nickel, aluminium, hydrogen, oxygen, carbon dioxide, sodium, calcium, chromium, titanium are found in these colours.

All kinds of diseases can be successfully treated by applying the principles of chromotherapy.

11

COLOUR-CHARGED MEDICINES

Colour-charged medicines come in three varieties – orange-charged, green-charged and blue-charged. Other medicines which are given to the patients include sun-charged oil, water, *mishri*, glycerine, etc.

Solarised Water

- Fill clean bottles of orange, green, and blue colour with drinking water, leaving 1/4th of the bottles empty.
- Close these bottles with lids and keep them in the sun for six to eight hours. Make sure that they are kept apart, so that their shadows do not fall upon each other.
- The water in these bottles acquires the medicinal properties.
- Solarised water is better than solarised sugar, though both have the same medicinal value when they are in the same coloured bottles.

Solarised Sugar

- Half fill the bottle with granulated sugar.
- Keep them in the sun every day, for a month.
- During night, keep them with their lids tightly closed, in a safe place.
- Shake them every day. Clean the outside of the bottles.

Solarised Oil and Glycerine

- Half fill the bottles with mustard or sesame oil.

- Half fill the blue bottle with coconut oil or glycerine or *ghee* (clarified butter).
- Keep all these bottles in the sun for a month, shaking them every day and cleaning them from outside.
- The bottles are ready for use after a month.
- Once in two to three months, keep them in the sun for four to five days.

Solarised Air

- Keep thoroughly cleaned bottles in the sun for five minutes.
- Then tightly close the lids and store them safely.
- These bottles containing charged air can be used, according to their colour, for asthma patients or for those afflicted with lung problems.

Solarised Honey

- For breathing ailments honey should be sun-charged for 25-30 days to get converted into an excellent medicine.

Solarised Vaseline

- Vaseline should be sun-charged for at least 50-60 days. Shake the bottle gently once or twice a day.
- During winter it should be slightly heated and then shaken so that everything inside gets properly prepared. The more the Vaseline is kept in the sun the more powerful it becomes. Keep cleaning the top of the bottle of Vaseline.

Solarised Ghee (Clarified Butter)

- To get solarised ghee the bottle containing *ghee* should be kept in the sun for at least 50-60 days and shaken daily.
- Clean the outside of the bottles.
- This medicine is prepared for the ailments of the delicate parts like nose.
- The application of this sun-charged ghee on the face helps to get rid of the marks of smallpox.

Solarised Green Medicines

- Green-charged medicines neutralise one's health problems.
- Being a combination of blue and yellow, the medicines balance the body's chemistry.
- They build and tone up muscles, giving them more energy.
- They purify blood and help in eliminating foreign bodies from the system.
- The brain and the nerve centres get stimulated.
- The green medicine should be taken on an empty stomach, or one hour before meals.
- Solarised green medicines are beneficial in curing indigestion and stomachache, diabetes, gonorrhoea, smallpox, fevers like malaria and typhoid, ulcers, cancer, high blood pressure, boils and pimples, warts, eczema, dry cough, cold and headaches, as well as ailments of liver, skin, kidney, eyes, etc.

Solarised Blue Medicines

- Being acidic in effect, blue-charged medicines are cool and soothing.
- They are very good antiseptics.
- Blue colour mostly affects the throat and the region above it.
- These medicines help in alleviating burning sensation in the body.
- They are good for controlling high blood pressure, hysteria and mental disorders as well as insomnia.
- They are also very effective in curing skin problems.
- Sunstroke, internal haemorrhage, high fever and headaches can be treated with these medicines.
- Excessive thirst, jaundice, food poisoning and poisonous insect bites can be treated with the help of these solarised medicines.
- Epilepsy, vomiting, nausea, cholera, dysentery, diarrhoea, etc. can be cured.
- To find instant relief from burns on any part of the body, pour solarised water or oil from blue-coloured bottles on the affected

part, and focus blue rays on it.

- These medicines should be taken on an empty stomach, or one hour before meals.
- Solarised blue air provides relief when there is inflammation of the nose.
- Solarised oil from a blue-coloured bottle helps in bringing down high fever.

Solarised Orange Medicines

- Orange-charged medicines are alkaline in effect.
- They have a heating and stimulating nature.
- Orange colour affects the abdominal region: stomach, liver, intestines, kidneys and spleen.
- Blood circulation improves greatly after using these medicines.
- Muscles become healthy and toned after using these orange-charged medicines.
- These medicines cure ailments like fever, pneumonia, influenza, cough, tuberculosis, nervous and heart disorders, paralysis, breathing and gas problems, lung troubles, etc.
- They help in weight reduction, remove weakness and strengthen the mind.
- They should be taken within 15-30 minutes after meals.
- Orange-charged air is specially good for lung-related problems.
- Oil from solarised orange bottles brings relief to joint pains.

Solarised Red Medicines

- Red-charged medicines are useful in low blood pressure and weakness.
- To uproot any ailment in the body this is an excellent medicine.
- It gives wonderful results in paralysis, joint pain, etc.
- Impotency can also be cured by these medicines.
- They are helpful in reducing weight and provide relief in hernia.

Solarised Red Oil

- In paralysis, massaging the affected area with sun-charged red oil of sesame seed provides relief.

- Using solarised red oil prevents wrinkles and small black spots on the body.

- For old coughs, asthma, pneumonia, etc., the massage of sun-charged red oil on the chest and back provides relief.

- For pus in the ear or deafness, sun-charged red oil of sesame seed should be warmed and put in the ear. Sun-charged red light should be used for beneficial results.

- The massage of sun-charged red *Ashirwad Mahanarayani* oil and passing red light provides relief in joint pains, pain in the waist, neck, etc.

Solarised White Medicines

- White water is germ free and so an excellent tonic for children.
- It can be drunk in place of plain water.
- It has no side effects.
- White water contains calcium and makes children strong.

Note: *The use of these medicines is extremely easy and in accordance with the laws of nature and are extremely beneficial.*

4

THE REMEDIES OF NATURE

There is a mutual relation between nature and man. It is a well-known fact that a human being takes birth in the lap of nature, survives, works and ultimately dies here. The human body is made up of water, air, sun, earth, ether, i.e. the five elements of nature. All these five elements at all times provides health to a human being. Nature has provided us eight physicians which give us health. They are – air, diet, water, fast, sun, sleep, thought and exercise.

1. Air

For the sustenance of life air is more important than water. According to the Vedas air is an *amrit*, and it exists in the form of life. Taking fresh air in the morning makes the metals and non metals in the body pure and healthy, gives intelligence. One finds happiness, peace and tranquillity in the morning air because it is clear, soft and fragrant, filled with the fragrance of flowers.

Pure air, water, earth, light and grains are called *panchamrit*. Morning walk is considered to be the best cure for all ailments. Morning walk and intake of air are called *brahmavela* and *amritpan*.

2. Diet

Body and food are deeply related. Every person should be a controlled eater because only a controlled diet benefits all the metals of the body.

Once the emperor of Iran asked his best doctor a question, "How much should one eat from morning to night ?" The answer was 6 dirhams which means 310 grams. He again asked, "How can that be enough." The doctor answered, "We should not eat more than that for our nourishment. Anything in excess only increases weight and decreases life."

A human being should eat less. Only a small diet is useful to the body. Only that much should be eaten that can be digested by the body. A pure and controlled diet provides nourishment, strength, age, satisfaction, glow, courage, mental and digestive strength. Diet creates the seven metals of our body. In the Upanishads it has been said that a pure food provides a pure starch and with the purification of starch, the mind becomes clear and strong. Then with a pure and strong mind one finds harmony with every object. Only that food is beneficial which is consumed when one feels hungry. Food should be eaten peacefully.

3. Water

Water is not only a necessity but important for good health. Drinking pure water after waking up in the morning is very good for the health. A person who drinks 8 drops of water before sunrise gains health and a long life. Well water or water kept in a copper utensil is good for drinking. One should drink water either an hour before the meals or two hours later. A person should drink at least 2 litres of water daily. This allows the blood to flow freely.

4. Fast

Dharama Shastras have given great importance to fasting. Fasting helps in eliminating the three-fold ailments of the body, provides strength to the intestines, and flushes out the impurities from the body. Fasting is very important for health. With fasting the spiritual strength of a human being grows. It is said that if one fasts twice a month on Ekadashi according to the given instructions then that person will gain control over his/her emotions and senses. Those who do not fast should initially begin with not eating food once a day every week and then start fasting for a complete day.

The day of fasting should be spent in praying and reading good literature and doing good deeds. It is necessary for those who fast to concentrate their mind on religious matters and obtain knowledge from saints and *mahatmas*. Such a fast provides mental and physical health.

One should fast for 12 to 72 hours to eliminate the enzymes especially the poisonous ones present in the digestive system. If possible during a fast one should drink lukewarm water and green juice. Every person should fast for 1 to 1 1/2 days every week without food and 3 days every month consuming lukewarm water, green water and fruits.

5. Sun

Sun is the preserver and protector of life on earth. If it were not for the sun we would not have been able to survive for a single moment. All ailments and germs get destroyed in sunrays.

For obtaining health from the sun it has been written in Atharv Veda "O mortal, may your life not be destroyed and this process of inhaling and exhaling while breathing continues. May the Sun God, who is the master of all living beings keep you high with his strength giving rays and not allow your body or life strength to fall."

Sun has a great effect on the mind and body of a human being. Medical science believes that with the consumption of sunrays every type of ailment can be eliminated.

6. Exercise

Ayurveda believes that a body develops with exercise, body parts lose their tiredness, one sleeps soundly, the mind stops wandering, one becomes active and the skin becomes beautiful and glowing.

In short, exercise provides energy to the body and increases the power of the body to work, helps to digest excess and unnatural food and the body does not feel lethargic. For happiness, health and beauty exercise is necessary in life.

7. Thought

Thoughts have a direct effect on the body. For mental problems a determined and controlled meditation is very necessary. Impure thoughts not only corrupt the mind but also make the body sick. Meditation and pure thoughts are a life force. So for an ailment free life one should take the help of thought power.

8. Sleep

Just as air, water and sun are necessary for a good health, in the same way sleep is also important. It has been said that if one sleeps at a proper time at night his/her body metals stay in position and laziness gets eliminated. Health, attentiveness, strength, enthusiasm and the body fire increases. A sound sleep is necessary for good health. One must sleep at night with good thoughts in mind. One must wear loose clothes while sleeping. For a good health proper sleep is necessary.

The benefits of sleeping at a proper time

- By sleeping at fixed times one loses all mental tensions and gets energised.
- Life span also increases.
- One gets relief from ailments such as night fall, mental deficiency, head problems, lethargy, etc.
- Body gets relaxed.

Before sleeping one should free the mind of all worries, tensions and fears and wish for happiness, courage and success. By this one can find a positive change in himself. By the above given eight remedies one can surely lead a happy and prosperous life.

5

HEALTH AND DIET

$\mathcal{D}$iet and health are closely related. Food provides body the necessary energy to do various functions. But a majority of us do not know which type of diet to take. In reality we do not know about the elements our body requires and from which source to obtain them.

Various types of eatables have different types of nourishing elements in them which are necessary to keep various organs of our body active. For example, milk contains a lot of Vitamin A which is necessary to protect the body against ailments. Its deficiency makes one sick and weak sighted. Our body requires a proper balance of proteins, carbohydrates, vitamins and minerals. If a proper diet is taken along with chromotherapy then it shows excellent results. It should be remembered that along with medicines a patient also requires a good diet and should take only a diet that consists of a lot of vegetables, fruit juices, etc. Heavy food puts burden on life energy.

A regular diet is required for old ailments. It should not contain refined or starchy foods like bread or polished rice. Pulses and grains should be cooked with their husk. Husk mixed in the grain aids the digestive juices on one hand and on the other hand clears the way for the food from the mouth to the kidney. Peels are disallowed only to those patients who suffer from swollen stomach or intestines or loose motions. As far as possible fried food and meat should be avoided. Fruits and vegetables should be eaten mainly because they are easy to digest and assimilate in the body quickly.

Tasty food keeps the mind happy and is also beneficial. In bile ailments foods which are cold in nature and in phlegm ailments foods which are hot in nature should be taken. There are six types of tastes—sweet, salty, sour, bitter, spicy, astringent

The digestive system begins with our mouth. Nature has given us mouth to chew. Make it a habit to chew every morsel 10-15 times even if it is soft and delicate. Those who chew fast consume excess sugar. Diabetes can be controlled by chewing food properly. Improper chewing puts burden on the stomach and when the stomach is tired it increases fats and gives birth to various ailments.

Properly chewed food provides more taste, satisfaction and naturally indicates when the stomach is full. Remember that we get energy from that food that we digest and not from excess or undigested food. If every person makes it a habit to chew the food properly then the food problem of the world will get solved. For good digestive strength the following points should be kept in mind-:

1. Food should be well cooked and eaten hot.
2. Flour should contain husk and only unpolished rice should be consumed.
3. Avoid fried food.
4. Milk, curd and buttermilk should be consumed more.
5. Only fresh and seasonal fruits should be consumed.
6. Solid food should be chewed properly.
7. The interval between two meals should be 4-5 hours.
8. Fast once a week or thrice a month.
9. Eat pulses with husks.

Taste is also an important happiness of life but the signal of nature should also be observed. With the first belch one must start stopping to eat and with the second belch eating should be completely stopped. The second belch clarifies that the stomach is full. Despite this clarification if one continues eating then this will be an invitation to ailments. Basically strength should be gained from the five elements so that the mind and body keep working efficiently. One should eat food for strength and not taste.

TREATMENT OF DISEASES

Headache

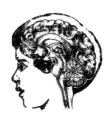

> * headache due to constipation * headache due to heat or fever * headache due to cold * headache due to heat or gas * headache of half side due to the accumulation of cough * headache at the back of the head * headache due to normal weakness * dizziness * headache due to sunlight * migraine

*H*eadache is one of the most common ailments among human beings. Headaches are caused due to many reasons – head injury, eye strain, fever, sinus infection, or allergic reaction, etc. Some of the headaches are mild, some are severe. There are two main kinds of headaches – acute and chronic. Acute headaches occur infrequently for a short time, whereas chronic ones occur frequently and last for few days.

1. Headache due to Constipation

Drink three parts of green water and one part of white water (up to 200ml) thrice a day before meals on an empty stomach. For people who are obese and have cough, equal amount of green and orange water should be given.

2. Headache due to Heat or Fever

In this type of headache equal amount of blue and green water from 100ml to 200ml should be taken on an empty stomach before meals and 5-6 drops of sun-charged blue coconut oil should be massaged on the scalp gently with the lower part of ones' palm and continue the same massage on the temple. This will provide relief.

3. Headache due to Cold

In this type of headache three doses of orange water should be taken from 50-100ml, ten minutes after taking the meals. The doses should not exceed the prescription because this will cause side effects like excess heat which can be cured by applying 5 to 6 drops of sun-charged green mustard oil on the scalp and massaging it gently with the lower part of ones' palm. The same should be continued on the temple also. The coolness of the oil will relieve the headache.

4. Headache due to Heat or Gas

According to their health, patients should take equal amounts of green and orange water from 100-150ml. Windy natured patients should take only 50-100 ml of orange water. According to the mindset of the patient the treatment is beneficial in heat and gas problems that causes headache.

5. Headache of Half Side due to the Accumulation of Cough

For the above stated ailment the patient must take 100-200ml of green water on an empty stomach before meals three times a day and drink 40-80 ml of orange water 8-10 minutes after the meals. This water is an excellent tonic. It should be taken for a long time and sun-charged green mustard oil should be gently massaged on the scalp, temple and forehead taking 5-7 drops especially more on the affected parts. In a few days this shall provide relaxation.

6. Headache at the Back of the Head

This is due to cold. Massage sun-charged red oil of sesame seed behind the neck slowly and pass the sunrays through four layers of red cellophane paper on the affected area for 5-7 minutes regularly for a week. Give 100-200ml of green water thrice a day, 20-30 minutes before meals and 40-80ml of orange water ten minutes after meals. This water is a tonic. The regular consumption of this water eliminates the constant headache at the back of the head.

7. Headache due to Normal Weakness

This headache is caused due to general weakness or excess mental work. According to the nature of the patient, sun-charged green mustard oil must be slowly massaged on the patients' scalp using the lower part of the palm. 100-200ml of green water should be drunk twice a day, half an hour before meals. Green water is a blood purifier that removes the injurious enzymes. Consumption of 40-80ml of orange water helps in digestion.

8. Dizziness

On getting dizzy one must gently massage 5-7 drops of sun-charged blue coconut oil on the scalp, temple and forehead with the lower part of the palm. This process must be done at least 2-3 times a day and one must completely take rest. 2-3 drops of the oil must be put inside the ear also.

9. Headache due to Sunlight

This is due to increase of heat in the body. To cure this 50-60ml of blue water should be taken four times a day and twice a day the scalp should be massaged slowly with 7-8 drops of sun-charged blue coconut oil using the lower part of the palm. This will provide relief.

10. Migraine

For its cure 100-200ml of green water should be taken thrice a day 20 minutes before meals. Take 40-80 ml of orange water 8-10 minutes after meals. This helps in the digestion of food and the development of red blood corpuscles. The scalp and the temple should be massaged 2-3 times a day with 5-7 drops of sun-charged blue coconut oil using the lower part of the palm for 10-15 minutes. In the morning and evening one hour after meals put a piece of cloth wetted with blue water on the stomach for relief.

Headache

Name of the disorder	Charged water	Charged medicine	Sunrays	Other remedies
Headache	Green & Brown (tonic)	Blue coconut oil	Blue	Put a bandage soaked with blue water on the head.
Headache due to heat	Blue	Blue coconut oil	Blue	
Headache due to constipation	Green	Blue coconut oil	Blue	
Headache in half of the head	Green & Brown	Blue coconut oil	Blue	Put a bandage soaked with blue water on the head.
Headache due to fever	Green	Blue coconut oil	Blue	Put a bandage soaked with blue water on the head.
Headache due to cold	Orange	Blue coconut oil	Blue	Put a bandage soaked with blue water on the head.

Name of the disorder	Charged water	Charged medicine	Sunrays	Other remedies
Headache due to congestion	Blue	Green coconut oil	Blue	
Pain in the back of the head	Green & Brown (tonic)	Green coconut oil	Green	
Headache due to general weakness	Green & Brown (tonic)	Blue coconut oil	Blue	Put a bandage soaked with blue water on the head.
Headache due to vertigo	Green & Brown (tonic)	Blue coconut oil	Blue	Put a bandage soaked with blue water on the head.
Headache if the sun is intolerable	Green & Brown (tonic)	Blue coconut oil	Blue	Put a bandage soaked with blue water on the head.
Severe headache	Green	Green coconut oil	Blue	
Headache due to heatstroke	Blue	Green coconut oil	Blue	

Ailments of the Eyes

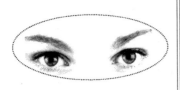

> * stye* redness of eyes   * cataract
> * swelling above and below the
> eyebrows * eye flu * hamaral opea
> * half sightedness   * pain in the
> eyes * trachoma

1. Stye

Stye is an infection of the eyelid which makes it red and sore. For its cure one must wash the eyes 2-3 times a day with green water and put 2-3 drops of sun-charged rose water into the eyes for relief. For the swelling one must apply sun-charged blue coconut oil on the external part of the eyes.

2. Redness of the Eyes

For redness, eyes should be washed 2-3 times a day with green water and 2-3 drops of sun-charged green rose water should be put into the eyes twice or thrice a day.

3. Cataract

Cataract is the clouding of the lens of the eye. Small spots in the lens may cause little or no vision loss. However, the spots can spread and make all or part of the lens opaque, resulting in blindness. The condition may affect either one eye or both the eyes. Its effect on the vision depends on the extent of the cloudiness. When this haziness starts in the eyes, one must take the sunrays into the eyes through 15-16 layers of cellophane paper. Remember that the sunrays should not be able to dazzle the eyes. Put 2-3 drops of sun-charged green rose water into the eyes 4-5 times a day.

4. Swelling above and below the Eyebrows

In this one needs to take 100-200ml of green water 20-30 minutes before meals thrice a day on an empty stomach. 40-80ml of orange water should be taken 8-10 minutes after meals thrice a day. The eyes should be washed three times a day with green water and two drops of sun-charged green rose water should be put in the eyes regularly 3-4 times a day.

5. Eye flu

When one catches eye flu one should wash the eyes 6-7 times a day with green water and 2 drops of sun-charged green rose water should be put in the eyes three times a day. Eyes should be protected from dust and sweat. If possible take proper rest also.

6. Hamaral opea

The main symptom of this disease is haziness in the eyesight. One suffers from night blindness which makes one gradually lose eyesight after sunset. Weakness due to various ailments and a faulty diet can also cause this disease. The patient should wash his eyes with green water 2-3 times a day and take sunlight by closing his eyes for 10-15 minutes. The rays of the rising sun must be taken. One must see the sun through 15-16 layers of green cellophane paper so that the eyes do not get dazzled by the sunlight. Take this treatment regularly for at least three months or more if required till the eyes do not become all right. The period of the treatment can be extended up to 6 months. If this period is still extended then it will be more beneficial. The cure is cheap, easy and without any side effects.

7. Half Sightedness

In this ailment one cannot see either the upper half or the lower half of an object. To increase the eyesight one must wash the eyes with green water three times a day and put 2-3 drops of sun-charged green water in the eyes. Apply sun- charged green ghee of cow's milk on the upper and lower part of the eyebrows. Give sunlight to open eyes through 15-16 layers of green cellophane paper for at least 20 minutes. This has to be repeated for a few weeks. Along with this, carrot juice should be consumed.

One can also take 100-200ml of green water on an empty stomach and 40-80 ml of orange water 8-10 minutes after meals. If this treatment is taken regularly one can get rid of spectacles within 2-3 months.

Eat 8-10 seeds of sunflower daily. Apply sun-charged red oil of sesame seed on the feet and rub the sole of one foot with the other. Do this until the feet get hot. At sunrise one must walk barefoot on the grass and drink carrot juice or carrot pudding and milk. Keep away from tea, coffee and biscuits. Have fruits for breakfast.

8. Pain in the Eyes

Excess work by the eyes, staying awake at night or due to some irritant in the eyes, pain can occur. If one has pain in the eyes then they become red, watery and dirt starts oozing out. Light dazzles the eyes and it becomes difficult to read or write.

In such a condition one must stop reading and writing and wear green spectacles. Wash the eyes with green water 2-3 times a day and take light from green cellophane paper. One gets relaxation from eye pain by putting sun-charged green rose water into the eyes 2-3 times a day.

9. Trachoma

To cure this problem one must take orange or carrot juice. Drink green water on an empty stomach 2-3 times a day and wash the eyes with green water. Putting 2-3 drops of sun-charged green rose water 2-3 times a day is also beneficial.

Ailments of the Eyes

Name of the disorder	Charged water	Charged medicine	Sunrays	Air	Other remedies
Sore eyes	Green	Green rose water	Green	--	Wash the eyes with green water.
All diseases of the eyes	Green	Green rose water	Green	--	Wash the eyes with green water.
Redness due to cold	Green	Blue sugar candy		Blue	
Nyctalopia	Green	Blue sugar candy		Blue	
Paralysis	Green	Green rose water	Green	--	Wash the eyes with green water.
Irritation	Blue	Blue water	Blue	--	Wash the eyes with blue water.
Pustule under the eyelids	Blue	Blue water	Blue	--	Wash the eyes with blue water.
Headache due to excessive eye work	Green & Orange (tonic)	Blue water	Blue	--	Wash the eyes with blue water.
Cataract	Green	Green rose water	Green	--	Wash the eyes with green water.
Falling of the upper eyelids	Blue	Blue water	Blue	--	Wash the eyes with blue water.

Name of the disorder	Charged water	Charged medicine	Sunrays	Air	Other remedies
Pain in the eyes	Green	Green rose water	Green	--	Wash the eyes with green water.
Redness	Blue	Blue water	Blue	--	Wash the eyes with blue water.
Black spot in the eyes	Green	Green rose water	Green	--	Wash the eyes with green water.
Long sightedness	Green	Green rose water	Green	--	Wash the eyes with green water.
Short sightedness	Green	Green rose water	Green	--	Wash the eyes with green water.
Sudden blindness	Green	Green rose water	Green	--	Wash the eyes with green water.
Squint	Green & Orange (tonic)	Green rose water	Green	--	Wash the eyes with green water.
Blurred vision or irritation	Green	Green rose water	Green	--	Wash the eyes with green water.
See different coloured stars around lights	Green	Green rose water	Green	--	Wash the eyes with green water.

Ailments of the Ears

> * pain in the ear * pus in the ear * dryness
> or itching in the ear * swelling * deafness
> due to pus in the ears * ringworm in the
> ears or eczema * tumour below the ear *
> deafness due to fever * boil inside the ear *
> * swelling on the temple bone

1. Pain in the Ear

Sometimes one suddenly feels pain in the ear. The reason for this may
be pain in the gums, jaw, and teeth, watery discharge from the ear,
etc. Dirt can also cause pain in the ear.

For relief one may put 2 drops of sun-charged red oil of sesame
seed that has been slightly warmed into the ears, once during day
time and once before going to sleep. By doing so one may also get
relief from any boil in the ear that bursts due to this cure.

2. Pus in the Ear

If there is pus in the ear then 2-3 drops of sun-charged blue coconut
oil must be put inside the ear for relief that comes after sometime.
This should be repeated for 1-2 weeks. There will be some itching in
the ears after sometimes.

3. Dryness or Itching in the Ear

For dryness or itching 2 drops of sun-charged blue coconut oil must
be put into the ear. Results will show within a week.

4. Swelling

Twice a day put 1-2 drops of sun-charged blue coconut oil in the ear and take sunlight inside the ear through blue cellophane paper.

5. Deafness due to Pus

If there is deafness due to pus then give sunlight through red cellophane paper for 15 days, 15 minutes daily twice a day to the ears. Then give sunlight through green cellophane paper for five days daily. Similarly keep alternating the process giving red and green light. During this process, twice a day put 2-3 drops of slightly heated sun-charged red oil of sesame seed in the ears and cover them with cotton. This will have a beneficial effect.

6. Ringworm in the Ears or Eczema

Twice a day put 2-3 drops of sun-charged coconut oil in each ear. For first two days put two drops and after two days one drop in each ear. Doing this regularly for a month will provide relief.

7. Tumour below the Ear

Many times a big tumour forms below the ears. The tumour becomes solid, swells and causes pain, fever and swelling in the throat. Even if the ailment is ordinary, it is extremely painful.

Rubbing the tumour with sun-charged blue coconut oil and drinking three parts of green water and one part of white water regularly for a few days will provide relief. Mud bandages also prove beneficial in this ailment.

8. Deafness due to Fever

Give sunlight through red cellophane paper to the ears and put 2-3 drops of sun-charged red drops of sesame seed. Doing this regularly for two weeks will provide relief.

9. Boils inside the Ear

Suddenly boils erupt inside the ears which is very painful. For its cure put two drops of sun-charged red oil of sesame seeds that has been slightly warmed and put cotton on the ears. Provide heat to the external part of the ears with a piece of light cloth or give sunlight through red cellophane paper. This will make the boil burst and provide the necessary relief.

10. Swelling on the Temple Bone

Give sunlight through red cellophane paper and apply sun-charged red sesame oil on the affected area. But the size of the cellophane paper should be bigger than the bone. While giving the sunlight, remember to make a hole in the cellophane paper through which the sunlight may go straight into the ears. At night apply sun-charged oil of sesame seed inside the ears and provide them warmth. Doing this regularly for 2-3 weeks will provide the necessary relief to the affected area.

Ailments of the Ear

Name of the disorder	Charged water	Charged medicine	Sunrays	Air	Other remedies
Pain in the ear	–	Red sesame oil	Red	–	Lukewarm oil
Deafness due to pus	Green & Brown (tonic)	Red seasame oil	–	–	Lukewarm oil
Buzzing in the ear	Green & Brown (tonic)	Blue coconut oil	Blue	–	
Itching and dryness in the ear	Green & Brown (tonic)	Blue coconut oil	Blue	–	
Ringworms or eczema in the ear	Green & Brown (tonic)	Blue glycerine	Blue	–	
Pustule and pain in the ear	–	Red Sesame oil	Red	–	Lukewarm oil
Boil in the ear	–	Red Sesame oil	Red	–	Lukewarm oil
Otitis	–	Blue pure cows Ghee	Red	–	Lukewarm oil

36

Nasal Ailments

> * old sneezing * coryza * sneezing, redness of eyes and marks on the face due to cold * growth of bone in the nose * watery discharge from the right nostril * breathlessness due to blocked nose and fever * bleeding from the nose * rotting of the nose

1. Old sneezing

If sneezing does not get a timely cure it becomes old. The nose gets blocked or the nose keeps flowing, the sense of smell is also affected there is headache, etc.

When the nostrils get blocked 5-6 drops of sun-charged green mustard oil should be gently massaged or rubbed on the scalp for 10-15 minutes using the lower part of the palm and 40-80 ml of orange water should be taken 3-4 times a day. If there is a watery discharge from the nose, then massage sun-charged blue coconut oil.

2. Coryza

In this ailment 40-80 ml of orange water should be drunk thrice a day and 10-12 sun-charged red *mishri* should be taken.

3. Sneezing, Redness of Eyes due to Cold

Usually standing while facing the sun cures the cold. For redness in the eyes one must wash them with green water and drink one cup of green water on an empty stomach. On catching cold drinking 40-80 ml of orange water is beneficial. For redness on the face apply sun-charged blue coconut oil. This will cure the sneezing.

4. Growth of Bone inside the Nose

Due to the growth of bone inside the nose one finds it difficult to breathe and breathes through the mouth. Chromotherapy has a miraculous cure for it. For its cure one must take 100-200ml of green water 20-30 minutes before meals. This is a good tonic. Put 2-3 drops of sun-charged ghee of cow's milk in the nose and inhale deeply. Do this twice during the day time. For quick relief give sunlight through blue cellophane paper to the inner and outer part of the nose. This should be followed for 4-5 weeks. The breathing becomes normal and this problem does not recur.

5. Watery Discharge from the Right Nostril

This is due to change in the climate or the room temperature. For its cure one must apply and massage 5-6 drops of sun-charged blue oil on the scalp, forehead and temple 2-3 times a day slowly for 10-15 minutes using the lower part of the palm. Take 60-80ml of blue water 2-3 times a day and 8-10 grains of sun charged blue *mishri*. This will stop the discharge of water from the nostril.

6. Breathlessness due to Blocked Nose and Fever

Apply and massage 5-6 drops of sun-charged green mustard oil on the scalp for 10-15 minutes with the lower part of the palm. This will make the blockage of the nose flow out. Use green and orange water as a tonic as mentioned before. This is an excellent tonic. This will clear the nostrils and bring down the fever.

7. Bleeding from the Nose

This is due to heat, wound or mental weakness. If so then one must massage sun-charged blue coconut oil on the head and give sunlight through blue cellophane paper. If sunlight is not available then put blue water on the head and use two parts of blue water and one part of green water mixed together. This will stop the bleeding. For the lost strength due to bleeding one must take 100-200ml of green water 20-30 minutes before meals three times a day and 40-80 ml of orange water 8-10 minutes after meals. This is an excellent tonic. This tonic provides strength to the body.

8. Rotting of the Nose

In this one must put 2-3 drops of sun-charged blue coconut oil in the nostrils. If this therapy is continued even after relief for some time then this shall eliminate the root cause of the ailment.

Nasal Ailments

Name of the disorder	Charged water	Charged medicine	Sunrays	Air	Other remedies
Old phlegm with bad odour	Green & Brown	Orange sugar candy	Brown (tonic)	–	Pass red rays inside the nostrils.
Allergy	Green & Brown (tonic)	Blue pure cow's ghee	Blue	–	Put two drops of clarified butter in the nostrils.
Chronic cold	Blue	Blue sugar candy	Blue	–	
Growth of the bones inside the nose	Blue	Blue pure cow's ghee	Blue	–	
Redness of the eyes due to cold	Green	Blue sugar candy	–	Blue	
All diseases of the nose (tonic)	Green & Brown	Blue pure cow's ghee	Blue	Blue	
Nakshir	Blue	Blue coconut oil	Blue	–	Put blue oil in the nostrils.
Phlegm, cold	Green & Brown (tonic)	Blue cow's ghee	Blue	–	Blue
Rotting of the nose due to wetness	Blue	Blue cow's ghee	Blue	–	
Sinus	Blue	Blue cow's ghee	Blue	–	

Name of the disorder	Charged water	Charged medicine	Sunrays	Air	Other remedies
Pustule inside the nose	Blue	Blue cow's ghee	Blue	--	
Allergy of the nose	Blue	Blue cow's ghee	Blue	--	
Nakshir due to getting hurt on the head	Blue	Blue cow's ghee	Blue	--	Put bandage soaked in blue water.
Bursting of nakshir due to blood pressure	Blue	Blue cow's ghee	Blue	--	Put bandage soaked in blue water.
Suppurate of the nose	Blue	Blue cow's ghee	Blue	--	
Sneezing due to cold	Blue	Blue cow's ghee	Blue	--	
Running of the left nose	Green	Blue cow's ghee	Blue	--	
Blockage of the nose due to cold and fever	Green	Blue cow's ghee	Blue	--	

Ailments of Mouth and Throat

> *pyorrhoea * rattling sound * ulcer in the mouth * muteness * dry cough * tumour in the throat and pain below the mouth * the swelling of tonsils in goitre * white or yellow phlegm * toothache * fever, loose motions and cracking of nails due to cough * worms in the teeth * swelling of the mouth * general problems of the teeth

1. Pyorrhoea

Pyorrhoea is a disease of the gums and of the bone that supports the teeth in their sockets. This is the chief cause of loss of teeth after the age of 35. The most common form of pyorrhoea results from the build-up of plaque on the teeth and gums. Plaque is a sticky mixture of food particles and bacteria. In this disease the teeth bleed, become hollow and weak, there is pus etc.

If the tonsils are old and phlegm comes out from them, drink 100-200 ml of green water on an empty stomach 2-3 times a day and at night an equal mixture of 100 ml of green and orange water (50 ml each) should be taken.

2. Rattling Sound

In this ailment one must gargle with green water 3-4 times a day and should also take sun-charged green *mishri*. Doing this for a few days will provide relief.

3. Ulcer in the Mouth

In this ailment one must gargle with blue water 3-4 times a day. Repeat it 2-3 times together. For best results one must have the water charged for 3-4 days. For complete relief one must put sun-charged blue glycerine inside the mouth and suck it. Spicy food must be avoided.

4. Muteness

Drink 50-60ml of orange water 3-4 times a day and gargle also. Put 8-10 grains of sun-charged red *mishri* and suck it.

5. Dry Cough

For relief from dry cough one should put sun-charged blue glycerine inside the mouth and suck sun-charged blue *mishri*.

6. Tumour in the Throat and Pain below the Mouth

In this condition one must rub sun-charged red oil of sesame seed below the mouth on the tumour and give sunlight through four layers of red cellophane paper. If the tumour is old one must continue this therapy for 1-2 weeks till one gets relief. This ailment is related to blood and stomach disorder. So the tonic of green and orange water should be taken regularly.

7. The Swelling of Tonsils in Goitre

In this one must gargle with blue water 3-4 times a day and put sun-charged blue glycerine inside the mouth on the tonsils and give sunlight to the affected area through four layers of blue cellophane paper. This should be done for a few days.

8. White or Yellow Phlegm

Gargle and drink 30-50 ml of orange water 3-4 times a day.

9. Toothache

To relieve toothache one must gargle with green water 2-3 times a day after meals and put sun-charged blue glycerine on the teeth and in the mouth.

10. Fever, Loose Motions and Cracking of Nails due to Cough

This ailment usually happens to those working with chemicals. If one suffers from fever due to this ailment then one must drink up to 50ml of blue water 3-4 times a day. On catching cold one must drink half cup of orange water three times a day. For heat one must drink 100-150ml of orange and green water, equally mixed 3-4 times a day. For cracks in nails one must rub sun-charged blue ghee of cows' milk on the nails 2-3 times a day and put the ghee inside the nostrils and inhale deeply. Green water should be taken as per the thirst. Taking this cure for 2-3 weeks or longer, will bring a glow to the skin.

11. Worms in the Teeth

Gargle with blue water 2-3 times a day. To remove the worm and cure the teeth one must apply sun-charged blue glycerine with a cotton ball on the area.

12. Swelling of the Mouth

Put sun-charged blue glycerine inside the mouth. Make four layers of blue cellophane paper and give sunlight through it to the swollen area.

13. General Problems of the Teeth

For the general problems of the teeth one must gargle 1-2 times a day with blue water and put sun-charged blue glycerine on the teeth and inside the mouth regularly. If there is swelling in the gums or any other type of swelling then the mouth should be opened and given sunlight through blue cellophane paper.

Ailments of Mouth

Name of the disorder	Charged water	Charged medicine	Sunrays	Air	Other remedies
Blisters in the mouth	Blue	Blue glycerine	Blue	–	Gargle with blue glycerine.
Pustules in the palate	Blue	Blue glycerine	Blue	–	Gargle with blue glycerine.
Chewing the tongue and lips	Dark Blue	Blue sugar candy	–	–	
Hole in the palate	Blue,green	Blue glycerine	Light blue	–	Put glycerine inside the mouth.
Bleeding from the mouth	Blue	Blue glycerine	Blue	–	Gargle with sky blue water.
Pus coming out from mouth	Blue	Blue glycerine	Blue	–	Gargle with sky blue water.
Hiccups	Blue	–	–	–	
Thyroid	Blue	Blue glycerine	Blue	–	Gargle with sky blue water.
Stammering	Blue	Blue glycerine	Blue	–	Gargle with sky blue water.
For the voice	Green & Brown (tonic)	Blue sugar candy	Green	–	

Ailments of Throat

Name of the disorder	Charged water	Charged medicine	Sunrays	Air	Other remedies
Wet cough	Brown	Brown sugar candy	Orange	Orange	
Sore throat	Green	Green sugar candy	–	–	Gargle with green water.
Dry cough	Blue	Blue glycerine	Blue	Blue	Gargle with sky blue water.
Whooping cough	Blue	Blue glycerine	Blue	Blue	Gargle with sky blue water.
Burning sensation in the throat	Orange throat	Orange sugar candy	–	–	Gargle with orange water.
Mumps	Blue	Blue glycerine	Blue	–	Gargle with blue water.
Tonsils	Blue	Blue glycerine	Blue	–	Gargle with blue water.
Glands in the throat	Blue	Blue glycerine	Blue	–	Gargle with blue water.

Ailments of the Abdomen

> * stomachache * flatulence* indigestion * cholera* jaundice * increase in the size of the gall bladder * loss of appetite * pain in the kidney * worms in the stomach * gall stone * kidney stone * ulcer in the stomach* yellow loose motions and fever * constipation and vomits after eating * loose motions * excessive loose motions * ulcer in the chest and swelling in the stomach * vomits of blood

1. Stomachache

For stomachache one must suck at least 8-10 grains of sun-charged red *mishri* 3-4 times a day and drink 40-80ml of orange water for relief.

2. Flatulence

To relieve flatulence one must drink 50-60ml of orange water 3-4 times a day. If this ailment is old then 100-200ml of an equal mixture of orange water and green water should be drunk and 8-10 sun-charged red *mishri* should be sucked 3-4 times a day.

3. Indigestion

If indigestion is due to heavy diet then 60-80ml of orange water should be taken three times a day and 8-10 sun-charged red or orange *mishri* should be sucked. If indigestion is due to heat in the stomach then the consumption of items which are hot in nature should be stopped.

46

Take only 100-150ml of green water once and orange water twice a day. Doing this for a few days will relieve this problem.

4. Cholera

Cholera is an infectious intestinal disease. It is caused by a comma-shaped bacterium called *vibrio cholerae*. The micro-organism is transmitted by water or food that has been contaminated with the faeces of people who have the disease. Cholera occurs when *vibrio cholerae* enters the intestines and releases cholera toxin. The toxin causes the intestines to secrete large amounts of water and salt. Because the intestine cannot absorb the water and salt at the rate they are secreted, the patient suffers severe diarrhoea. This loss of fluid causes severe dehydration and changes in the body chemistry.

To cure cholera one must take 20-25ml of orange water after every 10 minutes. Put some salt on a slice of lemon and suck it. One must take 3-5 sun-charged red or orange *mishri*. If the patient is weak then 150ml of the tonic containing two parts of green water and one part of blue water should be given to the patient to provide relief.

5. Jaundice

Jaundice is a yellow discolouration of the skin, tissues and the whites of the eyes. It is caused by the increased amount of *bili rubin*, a reddish yellow pigment in the blood. Jaundice mainly affects the functioning of the liver and the stomach. It causes inflammation of the liver. The symptoms are loss of appetite, tastelessness, stomachache, etc.

The cure of jaundice is very simple and effective. If jaundice is acute then one must drink 100-200ml of an equal mixture of green and blue water 3-4 times a day. Water therapy can also be taken with this. Hip bath and Sitz bath also provide quick relief. Do this for a few days and after having recuperated drink 100-200ml of green water before meals on an empty stomach and 40-80ml of orange water 8-10 minutes after meals. This is a good tonic for the body. Taking this tonic removes all the polluting enzymes and provides strength to the body. There are certain precautions one has to take – complete rest, intake of green vegetables, fruits like papaya, lemon, grapes, pomegranate. One should completely avoid tea and coffee.

6. Increase in the Size of Gall Bladder

To cure this one should take 100-150ml of an equal mixture of green and orange water 3-4 times a day.

7. Loss of Appetite

For this take the tonic of green and orange water as mentioned before and mix one fourth part of green water with blue and consume it regularly for some days.

8. Pain in the Kidney

To relieve the pain in the kidney one must drink 100-150ml of an equal mixture of green and orange water 3-4 times a day and bathe with lukewarm water for relief. After this one must regularly take the tonic of green and orange water as stated before and drink green water 1-2 times a day as per the thirst.

9. Worms in the Stomach

Heavy diet and wrong life style, eating too much sweets, etc., cause worms to develop in the stomach. The symptoms are – itching in the anus, bad breath, bitter belches, feeling of fullness, vomiting, etc.

To cure this one can take 100-200ml of an equal mixture of green and orange water 4-5 times a day. Along with this if sun-charged blue coconut oil's 5-6 drops are applied on the scalp and massaged gently using the lower part of the palm, at night regularly, one will feel relieved.

10. Gall Stone

Gall stone sometimes form within the concentrated bile. These small, hard masses may become stuck in the common bile duct causing severe pain. Blockage of the common bile duct may lead to jaundice, a yellowing of the skin due to accumulation of bile in the blood.

One should take green water after every three hours as per thirst. This will cause the stones to break up and pass through the urine. One must keep taking the tonic of green and orange water for further prevention.

11. Kidney Stone

Kidney stone is a hard object that forms in the kidneys. Most kidney stones consists of calcium salts. In many cases, doctors cannot determine why the stone forms. Some people who develop kidney stones absorb an unusually high amount of calcium from their diet. One should take green water after every three hours as per thirst. This will cause the stones to break up and pass through the urine. One must keep taking the tonic of green and orange water for further prevention.

12. Ulcer in the Stomach

For this give sunlight through green cellophane paper to the stomach and inhale sun-charged green air. Do this 2-3 times a day. Drink 100-200 ml of an equal mixture of green and white water 2-3 times a day. For stomachache one must take 40-80 ml of orange water 2-3 times a day or sun-charged orange *mishri* for relief. Do not take a heavy diet. It should contain more of green vegetables. Hot spices should be avoided completely for relief.

13. Yellow Loose Motions and Fever

In this ailment one must take up to 100 ml of blue water regularly for a few days 2-3 times a day and 8-10 sun-charged blue *mishri* should be sucked 3-4 times a day.

14. Constipation and Vomits after Eating

For constipation one must drink green water as much as one's thirst permits on an empty stomach on waking up in the morning. Going for walk after having this water will ease the constipation. For vomits one must take 40-80 ml of orange water three times a day after meals or take 8-10 sun-charged orange *mishri* 3-4 times a day.

15. Loose motions

Suck 8-10 sun-charged orange *mishri*, 4-5 times a day for a few days regularly. This will provide the necessary relief. After that take the tonic of orange and green water as stated before for a few days. This will ensure that loose motions do not happen again and the body becomes healthy once again.

16. Excessive Loose Motions

In this one can take 25-30 ml of blue water after every one hour and do this regularly for a few days. After some relief or difference one must limit the intake up to four times a day. Stop eating food completely. On feeling hungry take only the soup of green vegetables or *khichdi*. After feeling better the patient can take a better diet. For a week suck 8-10 sun-charged orange *mishri*. Give this to the children according to their age. Doing this for a few days will prove beneficial.

17. Ulcer in the Chest and Swelling in the Stomach

For ulcer in the chest one must massage the sun-charged red oil of sesame seed on the chest and back of the patient and give sunlight through red cellophane paper. Give the tonic of green and orange water as stated before regularly for a long period. In this ailment one can drink green water as per the thirst. This treatment must be done for at least three months regularly until one gets complete relief.

18. Vomits of Blood

To stop blood vomits one must drink 50-100 ml of blue water. This is a miraculous cure.

Ailments of the Abdomen

Name of the disorder	Charged water	Charged medicine	Sunrays	Air	Other remedies
Digestive power	Green & Brown (tonic)	Green & Orange (tonic)	Red	Red	
Pain in the bowels	Blue	Blue oil	Dark blue	--	Put bandage soaked in blue water.
Constipation	Green & Brown (tonic)	--	--	--	Drink water on an empty stomach in the morning.
Vomiting	Brown (tonic)	Orange sugar candy	--	--	
Cholera	Blue & Green (2: 2)	--	Blue	Blue	
Excessive vomiting	Light blue	Blue	--	--	
Nausea	Brown	Brown sugar candy	--	--	
Stomachache	Orange	Brown sugar candy	--	--	
Excessive loose motion	Blue	--	--	--	
Loose motions	Brown	Brown sugar candy	--	--	
Worms	Blue	Blue coconut oil	Blue	--	Put blue coconut oil in the anus.

Name of the disorder	Charged water	Charged medicine	Sunrays	Air	Other remedies
Indigestion	Brown	Red sugar candy	Red	–	Put bandage soaked in red water.
Flatulence	Brown	Red sugar candy	Red	–	Give red heat on the stomach.
Acidic belch	Brown	Red sugar candy	Red	–	Give red heat on the ribs.
Fatal hiccups	Dark Brown	Blue coconut oil	Blue	–	Give red heat on the ribs.
Hiccups	Light blue	Blue coconut oil	Blue	–	Give red heat on the ribs.
Loss of appetite	Brown	Red sugar candy	Red	–	Give red heat around the naval.
Dyspepsia	Green & Brown	Brown sugar candy (tonic)	Red	–	Give red heat on the stomach.
Heaviness of the stomach	Green, Brown	Brown sugar candy	Red	–	Give red heat on the stomach.
Excessive eating	Light Blue	Blue coconut oil	Blue	–	Massage the crown of the head with oil.
Excessive hunger	Light Blue	Blue coconut oil	Blue	–	Massage the crown of the head with oil.
Excessive thirst	Blue	Blue sugar candy	–	–	
Swelling in the stomach	Brown	Red sesame oil	Red	–	
Excessive dry bowels	Green & Brown (tonic)	Blue coconut oil	–	–	Put blue oil in the anus.

Constipation and Piles

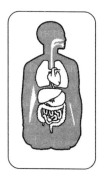

> * Constipation
> * Piles

Constipation

Constipation is a condition in which the bowel does not rid itself of waste materials as readily as usual. Constipated people do not have regular bowel movements, and may have pain over the colon. They may suffer from headaches and backache, sour belches and loss of appetite. Constipation can be caused by weakness of the bowel muscles or when a person uses laxatives too frequently or does not eat enough of certain kinds of foods especially those that contain fibre.

Putting the thumb on the middle part of the chin and rubbing it forcefully for 3-6 minutes on either side clears the bowel. For a good health it is very important that one should be free from constipation. When constipation results from a faulty diet the patient should eat more of green vegetables, fruits, whole grain bread and cereals, and other foods containing fibre. The patient should also drink ample quantities of water.

There are various such cures available for constipation. Drink lukewarm water and once a week give the stomach some rest by fasting. In constipation or such a condition one must put down the middle finger into a bottle of sun-charged blue coconut oil and then put that finger into the bowels as far as possible and rub the oil in the bowels. This process has been called *Ganesh Kriya* in yogasana. Only that food must be taken which is light and easily digestible. Drinking green water after getting up in the morning and taking a walk helps in the clearance of the bowels. Doing this every day will relieve constipation. Food should be chewed properly. One should also drink 1-2 cups of lukewarm water 2-3 times a day.

Piles

Piles is a condition in which the veins of the rectum get enlarged. Many people seem to inherit a tendency to develop piles. However, any condition that causes prolonged or repeated increase in the blood pressure in the rectal veins may contribute to the development of piles. Such conditions include constipation, pregnancy, and long periods of standing. Piles is also called haemorrhoids. Haemorrhoids of the internal veins may bleed or descend through the anus as a result of the bowel movement. Such haemorrhoids may cause pain and itching.

For its cure one must apply sun-charged blue oil with the help of the middle finger in the bowels as far as the finger can go before going to sleep at night. One must apply the sun-charged blue oil at the opening of the bowels. This provides quick relief.

Constipation and Piles

Name of the disorder	Charged water	Charged medicine	Sunrays	Other remedies
Piles	Green & Orange	Blue coconut oil	coconut oil	Wash the anus with blue water.
Secretion of kab from the anus	Green & orange	Blue coconut oil	-	-
Constipation	Green & orange	Green water	-	-
Absence of appetite due to constipation	Green & Orange	Green water	-	-
Acidic belch due to constipation	Green	Orange water	-	-
Piles with blood	Green & Orange	Blue coconut oil	-	Wash the anus with blue water.
Chronic Piles	Green & Orange (tonic)	Blue coconut oil	-	Wash the anus with blue water.

Problems of Sexual Organs in Men

> * less urine in summers * excess urine in winters * gonorrhoea
> * white gossamer on the phallus * pus in the urine * not sliding
> of the foreskin * urinary discharge in stoppages * eczema on
> the penis * impotency * infertility

1. Less Urine in Summers

For this ailment one must drink 150 ml of the mixture of one part of blue water and three parts of green water.

2. Excess Urine in Winters

If one passes excessive urine during winters then one must take 150 ml of the mixture of three parts of orange water and two parts of green water in the morning.

3. Gonorrhoea

Gonorrhea is caused by a bacterium called *Neisseria gonorrhoea*. The disease affects chiefly the moist surfaces of the sex organs. However, other parts of the body may become infected if the bacteria comes into direct contact with them.

In men, the most common point of infection is just inside the tip of the penis. About 3 to 10 days after infection, most men develop a discharge from the penis and experience a burning sensation when urinating. However, some men become infected without developing any symptom. This ailment occurs among females also and is especially serious for them. It can spread through the female reproductive organs and can lead to sterility.

4. White Gossamer on the Phallus

For this the cure is the same as stated above. The process should be followed regularly to be free from the ailment.

For this ailment one must wash the surface twice a day with green water and apply sun-charged blue coconut oil. Doing this process for at least two weeks gives beneficial results.

5. Pus in the Urine

When pus starts coming in the urine one must drink 100-200ml of green water 3-4 times a day. This therapy should be taken for 2-3 weeks and after that one must keep taking the tonic of orange and green water as stated before. This will ensure that this ailment does not happen again.

6. Not Sliding of the Foreskin

For this one must drink green water 3-4 times a day according to ones' age. At night one must apply sun-charged red oil of sesame seed on the penis and dress and immerse it in lukewarm orange water for 10-15 minutes. After that the dressing should be opened and the foreskin should be slowly slided backwards. After that it should be covered with sun-charged red oil of sesame seed. For complete relief this cure should be taken for at least 10 days.

7. Urinary Discharge in Stoppages

For its cure one must drink an equal mixture of green and blue water and massage 5-6 drops of sun-charged blue coconut oil on the scalp, forehead and temple slowly with the lower part of the palm. Doing this will cure the ailment. Taking this cure for at least 1-2 months will eliminate the ailment from its root.

8. Eczema on the Penis

This is due to the deficiency of Vitamin C. Constipation can also be its main reason. Due to this the blood becomes impure and the skin red and itchy.

One must not take pulses, curd, butter milk, raw milk or milk products. Antibiotic medicines, fishes, sour fruits should also not be consumed. One can take lot of *amla*, lemon, sweet fruits, green salad, green vegetables, etc. If the skin is dry then the oil of sesame seed and groundnut should be applied. This will provide quick effective relief.

For its cure one must apply sun-charged blue coconut oil on the penis twice a day. Follow a strict diet. If possible only fruits should be consumed.

9. Impotency

Impotency is the inability of a man to achieve an erection and therefore unable to have full sex. To cure it one must slowly massage sun-charged red oil of sesame seed from the area below the navel to the anus. One should abstain from sexual intercourse. Along with this one must take 5-6 grams of raisins that have been soaked overnight in breakfast. Drink the soup of black grams and boiled grams can also be eaten. If possible one must also eat 8-10 almonds every day. Keep the mind calm. Continuing this process for 1-2 week will help in eliminating this sexual weakness.

10. Infertility

Infertility in human beings is the inability of a woman to conceive or of a man to father children. Both man and the woman may be able to produce children with a different partner. For this reason, infertility is usually regarded as a condition of the two people as a couple rather than as individuals. Infertility may be temporary and treatable or it may be permanent. Permanent infertility is called sterility.

In some cases the cause of the condition can be traced to one specific disorder in either the man or the woman. But most of the time infertility results from a number of causes involving both partners. It may result from abnormal development, abnormal function or disease of the reproductive system.

Take the tonic of orange and green water as stated before for a long period regularly. Make small pieces of one fig and one date and put the pieces in a cup half filled with water for one day before eating them. After that milk containing sugar and cardamom should be drunk. This cure has to be taken for at least 2-3 months.

Problems of Sexual Organs in Men

Nature of the disorder	Charged water	Charged medicine	Sunrays	Other remedies
Impotence	Green & Orange	Red sesame oil	Red	Massage from naval to the anus.
Excessive Sexual urge	Green & Orange (tonic)	Red sesame oil	Red	Restrain massage of the abdomen.
Nocturnal emission	Green & Orange (tonic)	Red sesame oil	Red	Restrain massage of the abdomen.
Hydrocoele	Green & Orange	Red sesame oil	Red	
Sexual weakness	Green & Orange	Red sesame oil	Red	Restrain massage of the abdomen.
Increasing the power of the semen	Green & Orange (tonic)	Red sesame oil	Red	Restrain massage of the abdomen.
Sperm disorders	Green & Orange	Red sesame oil	Red	Restrain massage of the abdomen.
AIDS	Green & Orange	Blue coconut oil	Blue	
Early discharge	Green & Orange (tonic)	Red sesame oil	Red	Restrain massage of the abdomen.

Nature of the disorder	Charged water	Charged medicine	Sunrays	Other remedies
Deficiency of semen	Green and Orange (tonic)	Red sesame oil	Red	Restrain massage of the abdomen.
Weakness of the phallus	Green and Orange (tonic)	Red sesame oil	Red	Restrain massage of the abdomen.
Passing of pus with urine	Green and Orange (tonic)	Red sesame oil	Red	Restrain massage of the abdomen.
Syphilis and gonorrhoea	Green	Green mustard oil	Green	
Appendicitis	Green	Green mustard oil	Green	Put bandage soaked in orange water on the phallus.
White gossamer on the phallus	Blue	Blue coconut oil	Blue	Put bandage soaked in orange water on the phallus.
Absence of movement of the membrane on the phallus	Orange	Orange, Red sesame oil	—	Put bandage soaked in orange water on the phallus.
Flow of urine not smooth due to enlarged kidney	Blue	Blue coconut oil	Blue	
To abstain from sex for some time	Green and Orange (tonic)	Blue coconut oil	Blue	
Eczema on the reproductive organ	Blue	Blue pure cow's ghee	Blue	

Sleep Disorders

* Insomnia
* Excessive sleepiness
* Mental depression

1. Insomnia

Insomnia is the inability to sleep naturally. Insomnia may result from a number of causes – illness, coffee or other stimulants, etc. In addition, insomnia may be caused by psychological factors. It is often obviously related to conscious fears and worries. Sometimes sleep is disturbed by frightening dreams, pain or discomfort from a physical ailment, etc.

At night before going to sleep massage 5-7 drops of sun-charged blue coconut oil on the scalp slowly for 10-15 minutes with the lower part of the palms. After taking this cure for 3-4 weeks one experiences sound sleep.

2. Excessive Sleepiness

To cure excessive sleepiness one must take 60-80ml of orange water three times a day. One must also take the tonic of orange and green water as stated before for a long period.

3. Mental Depression

To cure mental depression one must take Sitz bath. The tonic of orange and green water as stated before must be taken. At night before going to sleep massage 5-6 drops of sun-charged blue coconut oil on the scalp slowly for 10-15 minutes with the lower part of the palms. This cure should be taken for six weeks. Take less and easily digestible food.

Sleep Disorders

Name of the disorder	Charged water	Charged medicine	Sunrays	Other remedies
Insomnia	Green & Orange (tonic)	Blue coconut oil	–	Put bandage soaked in blue water on the crown of the head.
Mental tension/ Depression	Green & Orange (tonic)	Blue coconut oil	Blue	Put bandage soaked in blue water on the crown of the head.
Blabbering in sleep	Green & Orange (tonic)	Blue coconut oil	Blue	Put bandage soaked in blue water on the crown of the head.
Feeling scared	Green & Orange (tonic)	Blue coconut oil	–	Put bandage soaked in blue water on the crown of the head.
Mental diseases	Green & Orange (tonic)	Blue coconut oil	Blue	Put bandage soaked in blue water on the crown of the head.
Weak memory	Green & Orange (tonic)	Blue coconut oil	Blue	Put bandage soaked in blue water on the crown of the head.
Fainting due to epilepsy	Green & Orange (tonic)	Blue coconut oil	Blue	Put bandage soaked in blue water on the crown of the head.
Restlessness	Green & Orange (tonic)	Green coconut oil	Green	Put bandage soaked in blue water on the crown of the head.

Breathing Ailments

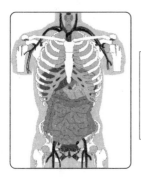

* asthma * cough * tuberculosis * chronic asthma * asthma attack due to breathing problems * tumour and goitre due to T.B. * tuberculosis in the chest

1. Asthma

Asthma is a medical condition of the chest that makes breathing difficult. This difficulty in breathing may affect an asthmatic person in sudden, sharp attacks that occur periodically. Symptoms include a wheezing sound from the chest when inhaling and even greater wheezing when exhaling. Patients may gasp for air and feel that they are suffocating.

Asthma attacks are caused by the narrowing of the small bronchial tubes in the lungs. This narrowing results from contraction of the bronchial muscles, swelling of the mucous membrane that line the muscles and the production of phlegm.

For the cure of asthma massage the chest and back with sun-charged red oil of sesame seed and give sunlight to the chest through red cellophane paper. Exercise taking deep breaths every day and take 50-80ml of orange water. If possible before giving the orange water the patient should be made to vomit by putting a finger in his mouth. After this the patient should be given 50-60ml of orange water. This will provide quick relief to the patient. This orange water should be taken 8-10 minutes after meals.

2. Cough

Cough are of two types – dry and moist. In dry coughs phlegm does not come out and there is a constant whooping sound from the chest. In moist coughs phlegm comes out. If there is pain in the throat one must gargle 3-4 times with blue water daily and put sun-charged blue glycerine inside the throat. For relief one must also suck sun-charged blue *mishri*. One should drink 50ml of blue water and put sun-charged blue glycerine in the mouth.

3. Tuberculosis

Tuberculosis is an infectious disease that mainly affects the lungs but can also involve other organs. Tuberculosis is also called TB. It strikes the people of all ages but is more common among the elderly and among those people whose immune system has been suppressed.

One can take 100-200ml of green water 4-5 times a day. More of green vegetables and fresh fruits should be consumed. The food consumed should be light and easily digestible. Twice a day the chest should be massaged with sun-charged green mustard oil and sunlight should be taken for 10-15 minutes through green cellophane paper. The tonic of orange and green water as stated before should be taken. This is a very good tonic. It should be taken for a long period. Green water is a blood purifier and orange water helps in digesting food easily and increases red blood corpuscles in the body.

4. Chronic Asthma

In this ailment the chest and the back should be massaged with sun-charged oil of sesame seed. Sunlight should be taken on the chest and back through red cellophane paper for 10 minutes twice a day in the morning and evening and sun-charged orange or red air should be inhaled for 5 minutes 2-3 times a day. Take a teaspoonful of sun-charged red or orange honey three times a day. One can also suck 8-10 sun-charged *mishri* after the meals. Doing this regularly for two weeks will gradually start providing the patient some relief. At the time of an asthma attack the patient should be given a hot bath. At breakfast one can have overnight soaked 5-7 raisins with milk without sugar. A proper treatment received for up to six weeks will lead the patient towards complete relief. The patient will experience complete relief in 15-20 weeks.

5. Asthma Attack due to Breathing Problems

The patient who has an asthma attack or has problems due to it should take bath 2-3 times a day. Twice a day he should take the solarised air. 3-4 inhalations of every charged bottle and the tonic of orange and green water should be taken as stated before. At night the chest and the back should be massaged with sun-charged red oil of sesame seed. In the day after taking the massage of sun-charged oil of sesame seed on the chest take sunlight through red cellophane paper and do some exercises. Doing this with complete faith will provide relief from all breathing ailments.

6. Tumour and Goitre due to Tuberculosis

For this one should gargle 2-3 times a day with green water and drink 100-200ml of it 3-4 times a day. Put sun-charged blue glycerine inside the mouth and rub sun-charged blue coconut oil on the tumour twice a day. Taking this cure provides relief from tumour and goitre.

7. Tuberculosis in the Chest

For tuberculosis in the chest one must take sunlight through blue cellophane paper on the chest and on the back through red cellophane paper and drink up to 250ml of blue water.

Orthopaedic Ailments

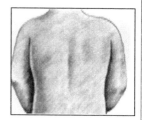

* backache * pain in the waist and spine * sprains * pain in the lower knee * pain in the ankle * tumour in the neck * severe pain in the knee * Joint pain * pain in the waist * pain in the shoulders * ache in the neck

1. Backache

If the backache is due to cold then the back should be massaged with sun-charged *Ashirwad Mahanarayani oil* and should be given heat. If the backache is due to gas then 50-60ml of orange water should be taken three times a day. Massaging the back with sun-charged red oil and keeping it warm provides relief.

2. Pain in the Waist and Spine

This pain is very acute. Due to it the patient experiences a lot of trouble. For its cure one must massage *Ashirwad Mahanarayani oil* in the afternoon and night and give heat and keep the waist and back warm. While giving heat the patient feels that small ants are slowly moving on his back. This means that the polluted enzymes of the body are coming out. This is a symptom of getting cured.

Note : This *Ashirwad Mahanarayani oil* is always available at Ashirwad Sunrays and Colour Therapy Centre. This oil is more effective and advantageous than *Ayurvedic Narayani oil*.

3. Sprains

On having a ankle sprain one must rub sun-charged *Ashirwad Mahanarayani oil*. After that the affected area should be dressed with soft and clean cotton. Give it heat and keep it warm. By providing heat at least 2-3 times a day one finds relief in only 2-3 days. One must also take 50-80ml of orange water three times a day after meals.

4. Pain in the Lower Knee

Due to cold and excessive physical work if one has pain in the lower knee then one must massage sun-charged *Ashirwad Mahanarayani oil* for quick relief. Remember to massage from downwards to upwards.

5. Pain in the Ankle

Pain in the ankle may be due to a wound or the polluted enzymes of the body. So the tonic of green water should be taken. Massaging the ankle with *Ashirwad Mahanarayani oil* also helps. Heat should be provided to the affected area.

6. Tumour in the Neck

Apply sun-charged red oil of sesame seed on the tumour in the neck and provide sunlight through red cellophane paper for 10 minutes, 1 1/2 hours after sunrise. At night the above said oil should be applied and there should be red light in the room. Taking this cure for 1-2 weeks will provide the necessary relief. Along with this the tonic of orange and green water should also be consumed so that this ailment does not recur.

7. Severe Pain in the Knee

To relieve pain in the knee one must take 100-200ml of green water 20-30 minutes before meals and 50-80ml of orange water 8-10 minutes after meals. This green water is a blood purifier that removes the polluted enzymes. This orange water helps in digesting food and increasing the red blood corpuscles in the body. Massage with sun-charged red oil of sesame seed twice a day and provide heat after dressing it with cotton. Eat light and easily digestible food. It is better to take foods which are hot in nature.

8. Joint Pain

Joints are often sprained or dislocated. A lot of acidic waste get accumulated in the body that it becomes necessary to first remove the polluted enzymes from the body and to do this the patient should take the tonic of orange and green water. This tonic purifies the blood. Food gets easily digested in the body due to which the body gets strength. Besides this one should take orange water twice a day. The quantity of this water should be 50ml. *Ashirwad Mahanarayani oil* should be applied on the joints. Exposing the joints to sunlight also provides relief.

9. Severe Pain in the Waist

The waist should also be massaged with *Ashirwad Mahanarayani oil* at night before going to bed. Give heat to the waist and keep it warm for some time. Doing this process in the afternoon at the time of taking rest will provide relief in 1-2 weeks. Keep taking the tonic of orange and green water. Observe strict avoidance in diet. This will avoid the recurrence of the ailment.

10. Pain in the Shoulders

Massage the shoulders with sun-charged red oil of sesame seed. Give sunlight to the shoulders through red cellophane paper. Doing this for a few days will provide relief.

11. Ache in the Neck

Massage sun-charged red oil of sesame seed on the back below the neck and give it sunlight through red cellophane paper for at least 10 minutes and continue to take the tonic of orange and green water.

Orthopaedic Ailments

Name of the disease	Charged water	Charged medicine	Sunrays	Other remedies
Hip pain	Green & Orange (tonic)	Red sesame oil	–	Keep the place warm.
Moving of the spine	Green & Orange (tonic)	Mahanarayani oil	–	Keep the place warm.
Pain below the neck	Green & Orange (tonic)	Red sesame oil		Keep the place warm.
Neck pain	Green & Orange (tonic)	Red sesame oil	–	Keep the place warm.
Cytica pain	Green & Orange (tonic)	Red sesame oil	–	
Pain in the vertebra of the spine	Green & Orange (tonic)	Mahanarayani oil	–	Keep the place warm.
Stiffness	Green & Orange (tonic)	Red sesame oil		Keep the place warm.

Skin Ailments

> * pimples * acne * ring worm * eczema
> * boils * white marks on the skin
> * burns * sun burn * cracked heels
> * chickenpox * measles

1. Pimples

Pimple is a red swollen blemish that usually contains pus. The most common cause of pimples is acne, a skin disorder which frequently occurs among teenagers.

To cure pimples one should drink 100-200ml of green water 3-4 times a day and apply sun-charged blue coconut oil and give it sunlight through green cellophane paper. Face should be cleaned properly with a mild antiseptic soap three to four times a day.

2. Acne

Acne is a skin disorder mostly among young people that produces many pimples. Acne consists of various kinds of blemishes mainly on the face, upper chest and back. A few blemishes are normal, but severe acne may result in permanent scarring.

Poor diet, worry and various bad habits are blamed for acne but they have little to do with the disorder. A balanced diet, enough sleep, and exercise and regular washing are good for the complexion and general health but cannot prevent or cure acne.

For acne also sun-charged blue coconut oil should be applied. Drink 100-200ml of green water four times a day. Face should be cleaned properly. It should remain oil free.

71

3. Ring worm

Ring worm is an infectious skin disease that produces round red areas, especially on the head and the feet.

For its cure the affected part should be washed with blue water twice a day and when it gets dry it should be properly scratched. Sun-charged blue coconut oil or Vaseline should be applied. Doing this for two weeks to two months will provide relief. One should also avoid curd, butter milk, raw milk, and milk products. Do not consume antibiotics, fish and sour fruits.

4. Eczema

Eczema is a skin condition in which areas of skin become red, rough and sore. The inflamed skin may be dry, swollen and crusty or it may ooze fluids.

If the eczema is dry then scratch the area affected so much that a watery substance starts coming out of it. Then wash it with blue water and apply sun-charged blue oil or blue Vaseline and give sunlight through blue cellophane paper. Doing this regularly for two months provides relief.

5. Boils

Boil is a painful infection of the skin and the tissue under the skin. It begins as a red hard lump. Slowly the centre of the lump softens and becomes pus. The bacteria which causes boils enters the skin through the hair follicle. Boils can be prevented by keeping the skin clean. For boils also sun-charged blue coconut oil should be applied.

6. White Marks on the Skin

These white marks occur due to some skin disorder. For this take 200 ml of an equal mixture of green and white water 3-4 times or more every day and take 50ml of orange water after meals. Apply sun-charged blue coconut oil on the white marks and give them sunlight through blue cellophane paper for relief.

7. Burns

Burns may be caused by heat from fire or other sources or by chemicals, electric shock, or over exposure to sunlight. Putting a bandage soaked with blue water provides instant relief. After that sun-charged blue coconut oil should be applied. It does not let any blister to arise or any mark to stay.

8. Sun Burn

Sun burn is a condition of having painful red skin because of spending too much time in the sun. Some people find strong sunlight highly painful which causes burns on their skin that leads to extreme itching. Apply sun-charged blue coconut oil or blue Vaseline 2-3 times a day. In this ailment the oil applied to the affected area becomes dry within minutes. This helps in quick healing of the burnt areas.

9. Cracked Heels

For cracked heels one can soak the feet for at least 20-30 minutes. This will remove the dead skin and then twice a day apply sun-charged blue Vaseline. Applying sun-charged blue Vaseline will provide relief to the patient and the heels will become soft and beautiful.

10. Chickenpox

Chickenpox is a common, generally mild and contagious disease of the children. The first sign of the disease is a kind of skin rash. Fever, headache and a general feeling of discomfort often accompany the rash. Red blotches first appear on the skin of the back or chest. They change into pimples after a few hours and then into blisters that enlarge and may become filled with a milky liquid. The blisters dry up in a few days and are covered with scabs. The skin rash appears in clusters. New blotches form while old ones change to blisters and dry up.

For its cure one should drink 7-8 glasses of green water according to one's age. Apply sun-charged blue *ghee* of cow's milk on the blotches regularly and give sunlight through blue cellophane paper. Doing this provides relief to the patients and the marks also disappear.

11. Measles

Measles is an extremely contagious disease that causes red rashes all over the body. The disease occurs chiefly in children but adults can also catch it. Measles is caused by a virus. People who have the disease spread it through coughing and sneezing. The first symptoms appear about 10 days after the virus enters a person's body. A fever, cough, runny nose develop and the eyes become red, watery and sensitive to light. In most cases a person has measles only once. During the disease the body produces antibodies. The antibodies provide life long immunity against it.

Slowly rub a few drops of sun-charged blue ghee of cow's milk on the head and face using the lower part of the palm for 5-7 minutes, three to four times a day. By taking 7-8 doses of green water as per one's age every day provides the necessary relief.

Skin Ailments

Nature of the disorder	Charged water	Charged medicine	Sunrays	Air	Other remedies
Different types of leprosy	Blue & Green	Blue coconut oil	Blue	–	Massage with blue oil.
Leprosy	Brown & Green	Red sesame oil	Red	–	Massage red oil on the affected part.
Pustules on the face due to cold	Green & Brown (tonic)	Blue coconut oil	Blue	–	
Pain in the nails	Light blue	Blue coconut oil	Green	–	Put bandage soaked in blue water.
Heat	Blue	Blue coconut oil	Blue	Blue	Put bandage soaked in blue water.
Corn in the heels	Red	Blue Vaseline	Red	–	Wet the corn with water and rub.
Sweating of the hands and feet	Blue & green	–	–	–	
Black head	Blue	Blue coconut oil	–	–	
Ringworm	Green & Brown	Brown, sesame oil	Red	–	
Boils and Ulcers	Green & Brown (tonic)	Blue coconut oil	Blue	–	
Eczema	Green & Brown (tonic)	Blue coconut oil	Blue	–	
Ring worm and dryness	Green & Brown (tonic)	Blue coconut oil	Blue	–	
Pustules coming out after itching	Green & Brown (tonic)	Blue coconut oil	Blue	–	
Secreting black pustules	Green & Brown (tonic)	Blue coconut oil	Blue	–	

Nature of the disorder	Charged water	Charged medicine	Sunrays	Air	Other remedies
Dhaffar due to exposure to wind	Green & Brown (tonic)	Blue coconut oil	Blue	–	
White spots	Green & Brown (tonic)	Blue coconut oil	Red	–	
Phulvahri	Green & Brown (tonic)	Blue coconut oil	Red	–	
Warts and pimples	Green & Brown (tonic)	Blue coconut oil	Blue	–	
Getting burnt from hot milk/real/water	Green & Brown (tonic)	Blue coconut oil	Blue	–	Put bandage soaked in blue water.
Insect bites	Green	Blue coconut oil	Blue	–	Put bandage soaked in blue water.
Ulcer of boil on the back	Green & Blue water	Blue coconut oil	Blue	–	
Boils with sores	Blue	Blue coconut oil	Blue	–	Put bandage soaked in blue water.
Burning sensation in the hot sun	Blue	Blue Vaseline	Blue	–	Put bandage soaked in blue water.
Chilblain	–	Blue coconut oil	Blue	–	Put bandage soaked in blue water.
Boil in the armpit	Green & brown (tonic)	Blue coconut oil	Blue	–	Put red sesame oil on it.
Boil in a hair follicle	Green & Blue	Blue coconut oil	Blue	–	Put red sesame oil on it.

Disorders of the Hair and Scalp

*hair fall *dandruff and greying of hair *baldness

1. Hair fall

There are various reasons of hair fall – mental tension, worry, anxiety, dandruff, lack of proper diet, some deficiency in the body, etc.

To prevent hair fall one should take a proper and nourished diet comprising green vegetables, milk, soya bean, butter, fruits, etc. Hair should be kept clean by washing them regularly. For its cure mix some soap powder with glycerine in water and add sun-charged blue coconut oil's drops to it. Wash the hair with this regularly.

2. Dandruff and Greying of Hair

Dandruff are small pieces of dead skin, seen as white dust in a person's hair. For its cure apply sun-charged blue coconut oil for beneficial results. But it is necessary not to use shampoo. Remember that the scalp should not be dry. If it is applied for a few days or until one gets relief all the above stated ailments will get cured. Apply soap containing glycerine on the head. On the head where the soap has already been scrubbed, rub mustard oil along with it and then wash it with pure water. After that the hair should be dried and sun-charged blue coconut oil and mustard oil should be applied on the scalp. This will protect the hair from dandruff or untimely greying.

3. Baldness

Baldness occurs if the follicles on the scalp die and no longer produce new hair. Heredity is the main cause of it but other factors like scalp infection, illness, reactions to certain medicines can also be responsible for it. If the baldness is hereditary then it cannot be cured. It is more common in men than in women. This ailment is due to paternal reasons, using each other's shoulders, washing hair with shampoo or using the wrong type of soap.

To cure baldness apply sun-charged blue coconut oil on the scalp twice a day while standing in the sun and give sunlight through blue cellophane paper for 5-10 minutes. This will cure the baldness and new hair will start growing.

Disorders of the Hair and Scalp

Name of the disorder	Charged water	Charged medicine	Sunrays	Air	Other remedies
Cracking of the lips	Blue	Blue glycerine	--	--	
Corn in the heels	--	Blue vaseline	--	--	
Blemishes on the face	Green & Brown (tonic)	Blue vaseline	Blue	--	Don't let the cheeks become rough and dry.
White spots	Green & Brown (tonic)	Blue coconut oil rough and dry	Blue	--	Don't let the spot remain
Lice	Light Blue	Blue coconut oil	Blue	--	Massage the crown of the head.
Black head	Blue & Green	Blue oil	Blue	--	Put bandage soaked in blue water.
Grey hair	Green & Brown	Blue coconut oil	Blue	--	Stop using shampoo.
Dandruff	Green & Brown	Blue coconut oil	Blue	--	Stop using shampoo
Baldness	Green & Brown	Blue coconut oil Green	Blue or	--	

Ailments of the Muscular and Nervous System

> * paralysis *unconsciousness *rheumatism *sprain * paralysis due to polio *epilepsy *inflation of the legs and veins

1. Paralysis

Paralysis is the loss of the ability to move caused by disease or injury to the nerves. In order to move, a muscle must be stimulated by nerves. There is loss of sensation in the affected parts of the body. For its cure one should stop consuming meat and intoxicants and take milk, fruits, green vegetables, unfiltered flour, along with salad, fruits, etc. Massage sun-charged red oil of sesame seed on the affected areas and take sunlight through four layers of red cellophane paper twice a day. At night one should massage 5-6 drops of sun-charged blue coconut oil on the scalp slowly for 10-15 minutes with the lower part of the hand. Wear red clothes. The bed sheet should also be red and it would be better if the walls of the bedroom are also red. Otherwise the bulb should be of red colour. Along with this the tonic of green and orange water is beneficial.

2. Unconsciousness

Unconsciousness is a state like sleep because of an injury or illness. An unconscious person is not able to use his senses.

Take complete physical and mental rest. Stay at a cool place. Sprinkling water on the face and other such cures are also beneficial. Take 150 ml of the mixture of one part of green water and two parts of blue water thrice a day. This provides quick relief.

3. Rheumatism

Rheumatism is a disease that makes the muscles and joints painful, stiff and swollen. It is a common term for all the disorders related to stiffness and pain in the joints or muscles. Common conditions that are frequently called rheumatism include *arthritis, bursitis, myalgia* and *tendonitis.*

For its cure take 100-200ml of green water thrice a day on an empty stomach 20-30 minutes before meals and 40-80ml of orange water 8-10 minutes after the meals. It should be taken for a long time. Massaging sun-charged red oil of sesame seed on the joints provides relief. Food should be light and easily digestible.

4. Sprain

If a sprain occurs then slowly massage *Ashirwad Mahanarayani oil* and tie a hot bandage. Remember that the bandage should not be tied tightly. Give heat from above and as far as possible keep the feet warm. Doing this 2-3 times a day provides relief. For sprains if other oils and medicines are used then there is relief in at least 8-10 days. But with *Ashirwad Mahanarayani oil*, the patient gets perfectly all right within 2-3 days and can do his daily chores easily. (*Ashirwad Mahanarayani oil* has a faster effect than *Ayurvedic Narayani oil*)

5. Paralysis due to Polio

In this ailment one should massage the affected areas twice a day with sun-charged red oil of sesame seed and keep the area warm. After massaging with sun-charged red oil of sesame seed, take sunlight through four layers of red cellophane paper for at least 10-15 minutes. Take the light of a red bulb and wear only red clothes. Take the tonic of green and orange water for a long time. Taking this cure regularly for 2-3 months will cure paralysis.

6. Epilepsy

Epilepsy is a disorder of the nervous system that causes a person to become unconscious suddenly, often with violent movements of the body.

The reasons are wound, fear, mental tensions, anger, etc. Brain cells produce electrical energy that flows through the nervous system and activates the muscles. The brain of an epileptic patient is not able to limit or control this release of energy.

For its cure drink 100-200ml of green water three times a day on an empty stomach 20-30 minutes before the meals and 40-80ml of orange water 8-10 minutes after the meals. This is a tonic. It should be taken regularly for a long time. Green water should be drunk as per the thirst and sun-charged blue coconut oil should be massaged on the scalp twice or thrice a day. This should be done slowly for 10-15 minutes with the lower part of the palm. Wear blue clothes, the bed sheet should be blue and a blue bulb should be lighted in the room. The food should be light and easily digestible. Cut small pieces of 8-10 raisins and one fig and soak them a day before and eat them in breakfast along with the water. They should be chewed properly. Drink milk with honey added to it. Always take green salad. Eat only green vegetables, coconut, carrot, fruits, etc. Taking this cure for 2-3 months provides the required relief.

7. Inflation of the Legs and Veins

For inflated legs and veins one should nicely massage sun-charged red oil of sesame seed once or twice a day. Give sunlight through red cellophane paper. At night give heat after massage and drink 50ml of orange water 3-4 times a day.

Pediatric Ailments

* bed wetting at night * child getting scared at night * stomachache * the crying of the child without any reason * headache * headache due to constipation * pain in the ear * pus in the ear * worms in the stomach * vomiting * sunstroke * loose motions due to indigestion * loose motions due to heat * swelling in the gums * yellow loose motions * teething * piles * coughs during infancy * water in the lungs * whooping cough * swelling in the eyes * uneasiness * weakness * chickenpox * excessive crying after waking up * fever * greying of the child's navel * cough * involuntary urinary discharge * rheumatism * anaemia

According to the sayings of Maharishi Charak the following reasons are responsible for ailments among children

1. When mothers do not breastfeed their babies.

2. Giving the child excess milk or too quickly also makes the child sick.

3. By giving cold food items to children.

4. The child also suffers from abdominal ailments due to eating mud or chalk.

5. Eating more of nutritious foods can also cause stomach ailments in children.

83

6. Not allowing the child to get proper sleep can also make the child lazy and sick.

7. Contact with a person suffering from a contagious disease or consuming a food or drink already consumed by the sick person may also make the child sick.

8. Keeping the child on the lap at all times.

9. Not rubbing oil on the child's body.

10. Getting breast-fed by a pregnant mother may also make the child sick.

11. It is usually seen that mothers make their children go to sleep by giving them opium or some other intoxicant so that the child may lie down in a corner and the mother may complete her household chores. But this causes grave damages. The child can also die due to excessive intoxication.

12. Bathing the child immediately after he has been fed.

Suggestions to Keep Children Healthy

1. The child's body is extremely delicate and it should be handled with care.

2. The child should not be made to jump up and down when he is being fed. This leads to the formation of gas.

3. The child should not be woken up from sleep suddenly because this can scare him.

4. A small child should not be left on the ground for long because the child does not have the strength to sit for a long time and may become crippled.

5. A child has a tendency of putting whatever he gets into his mouth. Therefore children should not be left alone.

6. The best food for a child is mother's milk.

1. Bed Wetting at Night

For its cure the child should be given a mixture of three parts of orange water and one part of green water according to his age. A child above one year of age should be given 2-4 teaspoons of this tonic and four sun-charged red *mishri*.

2. The Child Getting Scared at Night

A child should not be given too much food at night nor should he be woken up from sleep for his food. It is best to give a child a bath with lukewarm water and put to sleep on a warm bed. The bedroom should be open and airy. The child should not be scolded. He should instead be lovingly consoled and explained. Because at that stage the child is not completely conscious. After the meals, according to the age the child should be given four sun-charged red *mishri*. Along with this the strings of *rudraksh* or *munga* can be tied around the child's neck.

3. Stomachache

Give 4-6 sun-charged red *mishri* according to the age of the child and after sometime give one spoonful of orange water. This will relieve the stomachache.

4. The Crying of the Child without Any Reason

If the mother fails to understand the reason of the crying of her child she should put one sun-charged red *mishri* in the mouth of the child to stop him crying.

5. Headache

If a child has headache then 5-6 drops of sun-charged blue coconut oil should be massaged on the scalp of the child slowly using the lower part of the palm and also press the feet of the child.

6. Headache due to Constipation

When the child drinks excess milk then as a result he suffers from constipation, bubbles come out of his mouth, there is vomiting and diarrhoea. In such a condition the quantity of milk given to the child should be reduced. If the headache is due to constipation then sun-charged blue glycerine should be applied on the anus with a stick or finger. This will cure the constipation and 5-6 drops of sun-charged blue coconut oil should be slowly massaged on the scalp for 8-10 minutes using the lower part of the palm. Green water can be drunk 3-4 times a day according to thirst.

7. Pain in the Ear

If the child has pain in the ear then sun-charged red oil of sesame seed should be slightly warmed and 1-2 drops of it should be put inside the ear. Some heat should be given from above.

8. Pus in the Ear

Slightly heat sun-charged blue coconut oil and put 1-2 drops of it inside the ear for relief. This should be done for a few weeks.

9. Worms in the Stomach

If the child has worms in his stomach give green water 3-4 times a day according to his age. If thread like worms come in the anus then apply sun-charged blue coconut oil in the anus with a finger or stick.

10. Vomiting

If the child vomits then give the child orange water according to his age and make him lick powdered sun-charged red *mishri*.

11. Sunstroke

On getting sun stroke give the child blue water three times a day according to his age. This will give the child relief.

12. Loose Motions due to Indigestion

Give orange water 2-3 times a day to the child according to his age and make him lick sun-charged red *mishri* that has been nicely powdered.

13. Loose Motions due to Heat

Give 40 ml of the mixture of three parts of blue water and one part of green water 2-3 times a day for a week.

15. Swelling in the Gums

If the child has swelling in his gums apply sun-charged blue glycerine on the gums.

16. Yellow Loose Motions

Give 40ml of the mixture of one part of blue water and two parts of green water according to the age thrice a day.

17. Teething

When a child starts teething, there is pain, fever, cough, vomiting, etc. The child has green and yellow loose motions.

The child should be given 25ml of white water 3-4 times a day. His scalp should be massaged slowly with sun-charged blue coconut oil for 10 minutes. White water is a better tonic than gripe water.

18. Piles

If the child has constipation then it can lead to piles. The anus should be washed with blue water and sun-charged blue coconut oil should be applied on the anus as deeply as possible with a stick or a finger.

19. Coughs during Infancy

If the baby has cough then give 50ml of the mixture of 3 parts of green water and 2 parts of orange water 3-4 times a day. Make the baby lick 2-3 sun-charged red *mishri* that has been powdered and massage sun-charged red oil of sesame seed on the throat.

20. Water in the Lungs

If there is water in the lungs then sun-charged red oil of sesame seed should be massaged.

21. Whooping Cough

Whooping cough is an infectious disease, especially among children, that makes them have coughs and difficulty in breathing. Initially the child has trouble breathing due to an increase of mucus in the nose and throat and fever. At a later stage the child vomits thick globs of mucus.

For its cure give 3-4 doses of orange water and grains of sun-charged red *mishri* 3-4 times a day according to the child's age. Apply sun-charged red oil of sesame seed on the chest and back.

22. Swelling in the Eyes

The eyes should be washed with green water and 2-3 drops each of sun-charged green rose water should be put in the eyes.

23. Uneasiness

For uneasiness put one or two nicely powdered sun-charged red *mishri* in the mouth of the baby.

24. Weakness

The child should be made to lick one or two powdered sun-charged red *mishri*. This dose can be increased up to 4-6 according to the child's age. Continue this cure for a long period. Give the child green water thrice a day according to his age (one teaspoon of orange water for a child below one year of age and 2-3 teaspoons to a child above one year).

25. Chickenpox

In this ailment the child has red blotches on the back and chest accompanied by fever, headache and a feeling of discomfort. The red blotches become pimples and these pimples get filled with pus. The diet of the child should be taken care of. Sour eatables, curd, stale *chapati*, etc., should not be given to the child.

The child should be given a little green water 3-4 times a day and the massage of sun-charged *ghee* of cow's milk for beneficial results.

26. Excessive Crying after Waking Up

This is due to the deficiency of calcium because the child's bones become weak and they do not respond immediately after waking up. For its cure give white water 3-4 times a day and massage sun-charged blue coconut oil on the scalp slowly. Doing this for a few days will cure the ailment.

27. Fever

According to the thirst of the child he should be given green water 4-5 times a day. Slowly massage 5-6 drops of sun-charged blue coconut oil on the scalp. This will provide relief to the child.

28. Greying of the Child's Navel

Sun-charged blue coconut oil should be applied to the navel, press the navel to a fixed position, put a soft weight on it and tie. Sun-charged blue coconut oil should be applied to it and heat should be provided. This provides relief and heals the swelling.

29. Cough

For cough the child can be given sun-charged red *mishri* according to his age. This will cure the cough.

30. Involuntary Urinary Discharge

If there is involuntary discharge of urine then the child should be given orange water 2-3 times a day according to his age.

31. Rheumatism

Massage sun-charged red oil of sesame seed on the body for three months regularly and give 10-15ml of orange water 3-4 times a day for two to three months. Give 2-4 sun-charged red *mishri* for 20-25 days.

32. Anaemia

If the child is anaemic then he should be given sun-charged red *mishri* according to his age and 10-15ml of orange water 3-4 times a day.

Pediatric Problems

Name of the disorder	Charged water	Charged medicine	Sunrays	Air	Other remedies
Restlessness	–	Orange sugar candy	–	–	Crush one sugar granule and rub it on the crown of the head.
Pus coming in the throat of children	Blue	Blue glycerine	Blue	Blue	
Dental problems	Blue, White	–	–	–	
If children bite nipples	Blue, White	Blue coconut oil	–	–	
Averse to drinking milk	Green & Orange (tonic)	Orange sugar candy	–	Red	
Loose motions	Dark blue		–	–	–
Unnecessary crying	Orange	Orange sugar candy	–	–	Put sugar candy on the palate of the children.
Excessive crying	Green, Orange	Blue coconut oil	–	–	Put oil on the head and palate of the children.
Bed wetting	Orange	Orange sugar candy	–	Red	Put oil on the abdomen of the children.
Drying diseases (tonic)	Green & Orange	Blue coconut oil	Red	–	Put oil on the crown of head before the child sleeps.
Asthma	Orange	Orange sesame oil	Red	Red	Put oil on the chest and back of the child.
Palpitation	Blue	Blue coconut oil	–	–	Put oil on the crown of the child before he sleeps.
Children getting up crying	Green & Brown (tonic)	Blue coconut oil	–	–	Put oil on the crown of the head before he child sleeps.

Name of the disorder	Charged water	Charged medicine	Sunrays	Air	Other remedies
Deficiency of calcium	White	--	--		
Pneumonia	Green	Blue coconut oil	--	--	
Stomach disorders	Orange	Orange sugar candy	--	--	
Worms in the stomach	Orange	Orange sugar candy	--	--	
Dry/Wet/Whooping	Orange	Orange sugar candy	--	--	
Chickenpox/smallpox	Green	Blue pure cow's ghee	--	--	
Weakness of a six month baby	Green & Orange (tonic)	Blue pure cow's ghee	--	--	
General weakness of children	Green & Orange (tonic)	Blue pure cow's ghee	--	--	Give white and green water to the child
Secretion of kab from the anus	Green & Orange (tonic)	Blue coconut oil	--	--	
Cough in childhood	Orange	Orange sugar candy	--	--	
Water in the membrane of the lungs	Green	Green mustard oil	--	--	
Swelling in the eyes	Green	Green rose water	Green	--	
Habit of eating mud	3/4 white water and 1/4 Green water	--	--	--	

Women Ailments

* swelling of the vagina * heavy clots in blood * less menstrual discharge due to the weakness of the veins * excessive bleeding from the uterus * no menstruation * miscarriage * leucorrhea * red leucorrhea * itching in the uterus * the slipping of the uterus * infertility * irregular or erratic periods * tumour in the breasts * too much bleeding during menstruation* menstruation with pain * swelling after child birth

1. Swelling of the Vagina

If there is excessive swelling in the vagina then one should massage sun-charged blue coconut oil on the vagina. If the ailment is old then sun-charged red oil of sesame seed should be massaged to cure the swelling.

2. Heavy Clots in Blood

Here one should be given a mixture of 150ml of two parts of green water and one part of orange water thrice a day. Massaging sun-charged red oil of sesame seed in the vagina will cure the ailment.

3. Less Menstrual Discharge due to the Weakness of the Veins

Do not try too hard to put pressure on the veins and have a hot water bath. If the patient is short-tempered then she should be given green water thrice a day for relief and otherwise give 40-80ml of orange water, also thrice a day. Sun-charged red oil of sesame seed should be massaged on the vagina to give strength to the weak veins. Remember that the red oil of sesame seed should be charged for a long time.

4. Excessive Bleeding from the Uterus

If the body has excess heat then a mixture of 150ml of two parts of blue water and one part of green water should be taken 2-3 times a day and sun-charged blue coconut oil should be massaged outside the vagina. Try to feel if there is any glandular swelling in the body. If there is glandular swelling then it can be removed by operation. In the beginning this ailment gets cured by a hip bath.

5. No Menstruation

If a female does not have periods 100ml of a mixture of two parts of orange water and one part of green water should be taken. Sun-charged red oil of sesame seed should be massaged below the navel and waist to combat the problem. This should be done regularly.

6. Miscarriage

Miscarriage is the natural or accidental ending of the pregnancy before the foetus could live outside its mother's womb. The chances of miscarriage are most during the first three months following the conception when most of the females don't know about their pregnancy. Most of the time the cause of miscarriage is some defect in the embroy's chromosomes. Sometimes the uterus is not strong enough to withstand the pressure of the growing embryo. Excessive work, lifting heavy weights, hopping and skipping, having sex during pregnancy, etc., are some of the other causes.

To prevent the incidence of miscarriage Sitz bath with cold water and proper rest should be taken thrice a day. Massage the front of the vagina with sun-charged blue coconut oil and take 150ml of the mixture of two parts of blue water and one part of green water. Slowly massage 6-7 drops of sun-charged blue coconut oil on the scalp with the lower part of the palm and take proper sleep.

7. Leucorrhea

The symptoms of leucorrhea are pain in the waist and vagina, lack of interest in doing anything, loss of appetite, itching in the urinary pipe, change of the colour of blood to white or yellow, excessive bleeding, etc.

This disease is common among females above 50 years. A thick bleeding comes out of the vagina. Women who suffer from this ailment during youth have white and sticky discharge. Menstruation cycle usually lasts for five days. Sometimes the menstrual discharge is less or vice versa. In some cases the discharge continues in small quantities for 15 days. In that case it could be assumed that it is leucorrhea.

A woman suffering from leucorrhea should eat only those foods which are light and easily digestible. The food should also be nourishing. Bathing with fresh water and washing the vagina thrice a day with green water is necessary. The splashes should reach the interior of the vagina. It is also beneficial to take kati bath and water therapy for a few days. A morning or a evening bath is also beneficial. During leucorrhea oral sex should be avoided.

8. Red Leucorrhea

Generally there is a white sticky discharge but sometimes the discharge is yellowish red in colour.

To cure this disease one should wash the vagina and splash green water on it. Keep a cotton ball soaked in green water in the vagina. Keep changing the green balls 2-3 times a day. The cotton ball should be absolutely clean. This process should be done 3-4 times a day and 100-150ml of an equal mixture of green and orange water 2-3 times a day should be taken. Rubbing sun-charged green mustard oil in the vagina can give beneficial results.

9. Itching in the Uterus

If their is itching in the uterus then the uterus should be washed with blue water. 100-150ml of an equal mixture of green and white water should be taken at night before sleeping.

10. The Slipping of the Uterus

In this condition massage sun-charged red oil of sesame seed on the waist and take Sitz bath. At night before going to sleep massage 5-6 drops of sun-charged blue coconut oil on the scalp slowly using the lower part of the palm for 10-15 minutes.

11. Infertility

Infertility is the inability of a woman to conceive and a man to father a child. Infertility in females is due to many reasons like blocking of the fallopian tubes which carry the fertilised egg from the ovary to the uterus where it develops in to a foetus. If the infertility is due to swelling of the uterus then it should be washed with green water 3-4 times a day. If menstrual discharge is more or less then massage with sun-charged blue coconut oil. If the woman's ovary-secretion is lifeless then massage sun-charged red oil of sesame seed on the waist and below navel 2-3 times a day and take 50-60 ml of orange water thrice a day. There are different types of barrenness. Their names and types are given below-

1. *Adi Bandhya :* These women are born barren. They can never conceive.

2. *Mrit Bandhya :* Such females can conceive but the baby is unable to stay alive or is born dead.

3. *Kak Bandhya* : Such females can conceive only once in their life time.

4. *Vivrita :* Those women whose uterus is broadly spread are called Vivrita. Such females have their womb slipping.

5. *Pirita :* The woman whose vagina always aches is called *Pirita*.

6. *Vyagrini : Vyagrini* is a woman whose periods start after every 8-10 days.

7. *Shanda (eunuch) :* A eunuch does not have a vagina. She only has a urine pipe and does not have periods.

8. *Chalita :* The woman with a wrongly placed vagina is called *Chalita.*

9. *Tripakshi :* The woman who does not have periods every month but after every 45 days is called *Tripakshi.*

10. *Vimbhrata :* The woman who has suffered from leucorrhea or any such ailment is called *Vimbhrata*. Such a woman is incapable of conception.

11. *Lohit kshay :* The woman whose vagina pains at the time of bleeding is called *Lohit kshay*. Such a woman cannot conceive due to the pain.

12. *Sajja :* The woman who has *sajja* vagina does not have a fixed time for periods. Menstrual discharge is sometimes at the beginning of the month and sometimes at the end.

13. *Garbhstravi :* The woman who conceives but bleeding from her behind washes away her conception is called *Garbhstravi.*

14. *Trimukhi :* The vagina of a *Trimukhi* type woman always keeps on secreting a watery enzyme and it is never sexually satisfied.

12. Irregular or Erratic Periods

For irregular periods 50-60ml of orange water should be taken 2-3 times a day and sun-charged red oil of sesame seed should be massaged on the vagina. At night massage 5-6 drops of sun-charged blue coconut oil on the scalp for 10-15 minutes slowly using the lower part of the palm. At night light blue bulb in the room while sleeping. Drink 100-200 ml of green water 20-25 minutes before and 40-80ml of orange water 8-10 minutes after meals. This is a tonic. It should be taken for a long time.

13. Tumour in the Breasts

If timely treatment is not given then the tumour takes root and assumes the form of cancer. For its cure drink 50ml of blue water thrice a day. On the second day drink 100ml of an equal mixture of blue and green water. After two days for 3-4 days drink 100-200ml of green water 20-25 minutes before meals and 40-80ml of orange water 8-10 minutes after meals. This is a tonic. It should be taken for a long time. Rub sun-charged green mustard oil on the breasts twice a day. After that for 15 minutes give sunlight through green cellophane paper. Taking this cure regularly for 2-3 months will destroy the tumour.

14. Too much Bleeding during Menstruation

If there is too much bleeding during menstruation then 10 minutes before taking meals 100ml of an equal mixture of green and white water should be taken. Drink 50ml of orange water 10 minutes after meals. Massage sun-charged red oil of sesame seed on the back. After the periods massage sun-charged blue coconut oil on the vagina. This cure should be taken for one to two months.

15. Menstruation with Pain

For this massage sun-charged red oil of sesame seed from thighs to the vagina 2-3 times a day and sun-charged blue coconut oil on the vagina (not inside only outside). Doing this for a few days will eliminate the pain forever.

16. Swelling after Child Birth

Sometimes after child birth hands, feet and legs smell. For its cure 100ml of green water should be consumed 4-5 times a day. The tonic of orange and green water should also be taken for 2-3 months.

Women Ailments

Name of the disorder	Charged water	Charged medicine	Sunrays	Air	Other remedies
Menopause	Brown	Red sesame oil	Red	--	Give infrared rays on the abdomen.
Menstrual pain	Brown	Red sesame oil	Red	--	Give infrared rays on the abdomen.
Stomachache in pregnancy	Green & Brown (tonic)	--	--	--	Give heat on the abdomen.
Excessive or less bleeding in hysteria.	Green & Brown (tonic)	Blue coconut oil	Blue	--	Improve your daily routine.
Glands in the breast	Green & Brown (tonic)	Green mustard oil	Green	Green	Give heat
Breast pain	Green & Brown (tonic)	Green mustard oil	Green	--	Give heat
Mother who gave birth to a baby recently	Blue	Blue coconut oil	Blue	--	Give blue rays at night from the bulb.
Hysteria	Blue & Green	Blue coconut oil	Blue	--	Rub red oil on the wrist.
Fainting due to Hysteria	Blue & Green	Blue coconut oil	Blue	--	Put bandage soaked in blue water on the abdomen.
Less menstrual discharge	Green & Brown	Red seasame oil	Red	--	
Pain in hips during menses	Green & Brown	Red sesame oil	Red	--	
Miscarriage	Light Blue	Blue coconut oil	Green	--	Give light heat on the abdomen.

Name of the disorder	Charged water	Charged medicine	Sunrays	Air	Other remedies
Tension during pregnancy	Green & Brown (tonic)	Blue coconut oil	Blue	--	Please don't use shampoo in diseases due to tension.
Discharge of veth	Green	Green	Green	--	
Delay in menses from adolescence	Green Brown (tonic)	Red sesame oil	Red	--	
Itching in uterus	Blue water	Blue coconut oil	Blue	--	
Dislocation of uterus	Green water	Blue coconut oil	Blue	--	
Hysteria	Blue water	Blue coconut oil	Blue	--	
Infertility	Green & Brown (tonic)	Red sesame oil	Red	--	
Burning sensation in the breast	Blue	Blue coconut oil	Blue	--	
Glands in the breast	Green water	Green mustard oil	Green	--	
Irregular menses	Green & Brown (tonic)	Red sesame oil	Red	--	Give heat on the abdomen.
Excessive bleeding in menses	Green & Brown (tonic)	Red sesame oil	Red	--	Give heat on the abdomen.
Passing of blood clots from the vagina	Green Brown	Red sesame oil	Red	--	Give heat on the abdomen.

99

Fever

> * influenza * high fever * pneumonia * fever due to heat
> * fever due to cold * malarial fever * fever in the evening and loss
> of sleep * seasonal fever

1. Influenza

Influenza is also known as flu. It is an infectious disease like a very bad cold, that causes fever, pains and weakness. Influenza is caused by a virus. It is mainly a respiratory disease. The virus is inhaled and comes in contact with cells of the upper air passage.

For its cure make the patient lie down comfortably on the bed and keep the windows open in such a way that the polluted air from inside keeps going out but the patient should not be affected by the direct winds. In high fever massage 5-6 drops of sun-charged blue coconut oil on the scalp slowly for 10-15 minutes using the lower part of the palm. One should continuously drink green water as per thirst or 5-6 times a day. This will provide relief. The head should not be massaged with blue coconut oil. Light and easily digestible food should be taken.

2. High Fever

In high fever slowly massage 5-6 drops of sun-charged blue coconut oil on the scalp for 10-15 minutes using the lower part of the palm. Drink up to 100ml of green water 5-6 times a day. When the fever comes down drink only green water.

3. Pneumonia

Pneumonia is a serious illness affecting one or both the lungs that makes breathing difficult. It results from infection by viruses, bacteria, fungi, or other microbes. The symptoms are sudden attacks of chills, high fever, chest pain.

For the cure of fever due to pneumonia the chest should be massaged with sun-charged red oil of sesame seed. If possible give sunlight through four layers of red cellophane paper for 5-7 minutes. Drink up to 50ml of orange water three times a day. For bringing down the fever slowly massage 5-6 drops of sun-charged blue coconut oil on the scalp for 10-15 minutes using the lower part of the palm.

4. Fever due to Heat

The symptoms are shiver, sweating, excess thirst, uneasiness, pain in the forehead especially in the eyebrows.

To cure this fever massage 5-6 drops of sun-charged blue coconut oil on the scalp and forehead slowly for 10-15 minutes using the lower part of the palm. Drink 50-100 ml of blue water 3-4 times a day.

5. Fever due to Cold

The symptoms are headache, sneezing, stiffness of the body, watery eyes, chest pain due to coughs, loose motions, etc.

To cure this fever sun-charged blue medicine or blue water should not be used. In this type of fever only green water should be taken. In high fever massage 5-6 drops of sun-charged blue coconut oil on the scalp slowly for 10-15 minutes using the lower part of the palm. Foot bath should be taken for 15 minutes. Then dry it with a towel and take rest for some time. If their is pain in the chest then a massage of 1-2 drops of sun-charged red oil of sesame seed provides relief.

6. Malarial Fever

Malaria is a disease that causes fever and shivering and is caused by the bite of some types of mosquitoes. Malarial attack lasts for two to three hours and is accompanied by headache, muscular pain, and nausea. If the fever is high then drink blue water and massage 5-6 drops of sun-charged blue coconut oil on the scalp slowly for 10-15 minutes using the lower part of the palm. This will cure the fever.

7. Fever in the Evening and Loss of Sleep

If the fever is between 99°C to 100°C then the hands and feet remain cold and the body remains hot. Drink a large quantity of green water according to the thirst 4-5 times a day and inhale air through empty green bottle and take hip bath. Avoid eating meat, fish, tea, etc. If one finds it difficult to sleep then massage 5-6 drops of sun-charged blue coconut oil on the scalp and temple slowly for 10-15 minutes. This will provide sound sleep.

8. Seasonal Fever

This fever happens due to change in season. In this one should drink green water 4-5 times a day according to the thirst until one becomes healthy once again. After that take 100-150ml of green water on an empty stomach 20-25 minutes before meals and 40-80ml of orange water 8-10 minutes after the meals.

Fever

TREATMENT OF DISEASES

Name of the disorder	Charged water	Charged medicine	Sunrays	Air	Other remedies
Pneumonia	Green	Green mustard oil	Green	Green	Put bandage soaked in green/blue water on the head.
Malaria	Green	Blue coconut oil	-	-	Put bandage soaked in green/blue water on the head.
Delirium	Green	Blue coconut oil	Green	-	Put bandage soaked in green/blue water on the head.
Seasonal fever	Green	Blue coconut oil	-	-	
Fever due to heat and cold	Blue	Blue sugar candy	Blue	-	
Dengu fever	Green & blue (2 : 2)	Blue coconut oil	Blue	Blue	Put bandage soaked in green/blue water on the head.
Body pain in fever	Green & Orange (tonic)	Red sesame oil	Green	-	Massage the body.
High temperature	Green	Blue coconut oil	Blue	-	Put bandage soaked in green/blue water on the head.
Slight temperature	Green	-	-	-	
Fever in the evening	Green & Orange (3 : 1)	-	-	-	
Tuberculosis from fever	Green & Orange (tonic)	Red sesame oil	Red	Red	Put oil on the chest.
Weakness in fever	Green & Orange (tonic)	Blue coconut oil	-	-	

Blood Pressure

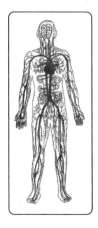

> * High blood pressure * Low blood pressure

Blood pressure is the pressure exerted by the blood on the walls of the arteries. The amount of pressure depends on the strength and rate of the contraction of the heart, the amount of blood present in the circulatory system and the elasticity of the arteries.

1. High Blood Pressure or Hypertension

Hypertension is a medical term for the disease commonly called high blood pressure. High blood pressure is the main cause of heart attacks, strokes and kidney failures. As people become older their blood pressure rises because their arteries become less elastic and the blood flows slowly. Some other reasons for high blood pressure are illnesses like kidney disease or overactive adrenal glands.

To cure high blood pressure one should take 100-200ml of green water 3-4 times a day. Massage 5-6 drops of sun-charged blue coconut oil on the forehead and temple slowly using the lower part of the palm for 5-10 minutes. After doing this regularly for a few days when the blood pressure comes under some control then start drinking 100-200ml of green water 20-25 minutes before meals and 40-80ml of orange water 8-10 minutes after meals. This is a tonic. It should be taken for a long time regularly and continuously. This will keep the blood pressure under control.

2. Low Blood Pressure or Hypotension

To treat low blood pressure drink at least 200ml of an equal mixture of green and white water 4-5 times a day and twice a day drink up to 50ml of orange water. In the morning and evening instead of tea drink hot water mixed with honey and lime. Massage sun-charged red oil of sesame seed on the legs. Massage upwards on the backside of the legs.

Blood Pressure

Name of the disorder	Charged water	Charged medicine	Sunrays	Air	Other remedies
Low blood pressure	Green & Brown (tonic)	Blue coconut oil	Blue	–	
High blood pressure	Green & Brown (tonic)	Blue coconut oil	Blue	–	
Mental tension and allergy in high blood pressure	Green & Brown (tonic)	Blue coconut oil	Blue	–	
Tension and allergy	Green & Brown (tonic)	Blue coconut oil	Blue	–	
High blood pressure in diabetes	Green & Brown (tonic)	Blue coconut oil	Blue	–	
Diabetes and anemia in People with low blood pressure	Green & Brown (tonic)	Blue coconut oil	Blue	–	

Ailments of the Heart

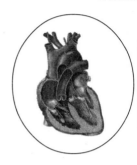

*heart failure *heart attack *inflammatory heart disease *blockage of the blood flow *causes of heart ailments

1. Heart Failure

Heart failure is a condition in which the heart pumps blood inefficiently. It does not mean that the heart stops beating. Any disease that hampers the heart's ability to deliver blood to the body may cause it.

2. Heart Attack

Heart attacks occur when a blood clot suddenly and completely blocks a coronary artery. Before a heart attack many people suffer from angina, feel dizzy, have indigestion or experience other symptoms.

3. Inflammatory Heart Disease

Inflammatory heart disease, which involves swelling, heat, and pain, can strike various parts of the heart.

4. Blockage of the Blood Flow

It is a common congenital heart defect. One reason could be that the aortic valve has two flaps instead of three.

According to Acharya Shutrut there are three reasons for all heart ailments – infection, heat, coldness. Different symptoms have been mentioned for the above stated three types.

i. *The symptoms of heart ailments due to infection*

A vacuum is created in the heart because of gas and one experiences dryness and there is pain in the heart.

ii. *The symptoms of heart ailments due to heat*

Everything around appears dark, one experiences heat in the body especially in the heart, there is increase in temperature, the body turns yellow, etc.

iii. *The symptoms of heart ailments due to coldness*

One feels heavy, there is accumulation of phlegm, fever, etc. Maharishi Acharya Charak has stated different methods to cure different heart ailments. One easiest cure which he has given for all the ailments of the heart is green water as it is a blood purifier. It helps in removing the polluted enzymes from the body. Blue water is beneficial for ailments due to heat. Orange water is helpful in heart ailments due to coldness.

Causes of Heart Ailments

Mental tension and sleeplessness

If one suffers from sleeplessness then he should drink 100-200ml of green water 20-25 minutes before meals and 40-80ml of orange water 8-10 minutes after meals. Once a day give sunlight through red cellophane paper behind the neck for 5-10 minutes. Massage 5-6 drops of sun-charged blue coconut oil on the scalp, forehead and temple for 5-10 minutes using the lower part of the palm and sun-charged green mustard oil on the soles of the feet and take a foot bath. Doing this will give relief from mental tensions and sleeplessness. Going for walks can also help. Walking on green grass in the morning is extremely good. One should only eat easily digestible food.

Obesity

Obesity can lead to disease of heart and blood vessels especially coronary heart disease. One should drink 100-200ml of green water 20-25 minutes before meals and drink up to 40-80ml of orange water 8-10 minutes after meals. It should be taken for a longer period. Eat foods that are easily digestible. Avoid potatoes, rice, fried foods, etc.

Ailments of the Heart

Name of the disorder	Charged water	Charged medicine	Sunrays	Air	Other remedies
Burning sensation in the heart	Green & Brown (tonic)	Green mustard oil	Dark blue	--	Put bandage soaked in green water.
Abnormal heart rhythms	Green & Brown	Green mustard oil (tonic)	Green	--	Put bandage soaked in green water.
Pain in the heart	Green & Brown	Green mustard oil (tonic)	Green	--	Put bandage soaked in green water.
Heart failure	Green & Brown	Green mustard oil (tonic)	Green	--	Put bandage soaked in green water.

Diabetes

Diabetes is a medical condition, caused by a lack of insulin, which makes the patient produce a lot of urine. The cause of diabetes is unknown. The disease is common in some families but many diabetics have a known family history of diabetes. The body of a diabetic person is slow in using glucose and so glucose builds up in the body. There are two types of diabetes – Type I diabetes (insulin dependent) and Type II diabetes (non-insulin dependent). In the insulin dependent diabetes there is lack of insulin and in the non-insulin dependent diabetes there is above normal production of insulin. Insulin which is produced by the pancreas enables the body to use and store glucose quickly.

Symptoms of Diabetes

The symptoms of diabetes include excessive urination, great thirst, hunger, and loss of weight and strength. These symptoms may appear gradually – and even be unnoticed – in Type II diabetes. This kind of diabetes is most common in overweight individuals above 40 years of age.

Diabetes cannot be cured, but proper treatment can improve a patient's condition considerably. Many diabetics live almost as long as people of normal health. For its cure take 1/2 glass of green water every day in the morning on an empty stomach. This improves the working of the kidney, intestine and in this way it is helpful to remove the polluted enzymes from the blood. One should drink 100-200ml of green water 20-25 minutes before meals and 40-80ml of orange water 8-10 minutes after meals. This is a tonic. It should be taken for a long period.

Note: The patients who have been taking insulin and have started taking chromotherapy should not stop taking insulin suddenly and take the above stated sun-charged medicines.

Green water being a blood purifier removes the polluted elements in blood and improves the working of kidneys and intestines. Orange water helps in digesting food quickly and increases the red blood corpuscles in the body.

Following things should be followed by a patient of diabetes:

1. Fast once or twice a day.
2. Take a walk twice a day in the morning and evening.
3. Eat rose apples, fresh lady fingers and raw vegetables.
4. Take the juice of bitter gourd or a powder made of dry bitter gourd.
5. Eat the chutney of coriander regularly for 40 days. Eating this normalises the cholesterol. Cook and eat it according to your taste.
6. Soak dry fenugreek overnight and drink its water when you get up in the morning and eat the *chapati* of fenugreek made with basil or maize flour.
7. Grind seven leaves of *neem*, basil and seven grains of black pepper. Taking this proves useful.
8. Eat the chutney of *amla*.
9. Dry five leaves of rose apple in shade, make them into powder and take it twice a day along with green water. This will completely cure diabetes.
10. For relief in diabetes one should have a sun bath twice a day daily and do light exercises at least twice a day.
11. Massage your entire body with your hands with or without the use of oil.
12. Do *surya namaskar*. This contains all *yogasanas*. *Pranayama* also gives good results.
13. Boil the chaff of wheat and filter it after it has been soaked overnight. Drink its water. This water should be taken 7 days in the first week, 5 days in the second week, 4 days in the third week, 2 days in the fourth week and then this should be continued with two days a week regularly for beneficial results.

14. To reduce cholesterol take a spoonful of grounded coriander with green water or boil three tablespoons of grounded coriander in 4 glasses of water and reduce this mixture to 2 glasses. Drink this water for two weeks.

15. Drink 100-200ml of green water 20-25 minutes before meals and 40-80ml of orange water 8-10 minutes after meals. This is a tonic. It should be taken for a long period. It is economical, effective and without any side effects.

Diabetics should avoid potatoes, bananas, grapes, custard apple, sweet potato, *chikoo,* mango, sugar, pastry, cold drinks, fried foods, tea, coffee, sweets, pudding, alcohol, cigarette, excess *chapati.* Water should not be taken along with *chapati.* Food should be eaten regularly. Foods containing starch should be avoided.

One should drink the soup of black gram with a little salt. Grind sprouted grams, sprouted pulses and fried black grams and make them into powder. This can be taken as *sattu.*

Complications due to diabetes or effects of diabetes

1. *High Blood Sugar*
In high blood sugar the patient should take 100-200ml of green water 20-25 minutes before meals and 40-80ml of orange water 8-10 minutes after meals. This is a tonic. This should be taken for a long period. Strict avoidance should be maintained in diet.

2. *Tension*
For tension massage 5-6 drops of sun-charged blue coconut oil twice a day slowly using the lower part of the palm for 15-20 minutes. Do this in the afternoon and take rest after that. This will slowly and gradually reduce tension and after some tension gets reduced start massaging this blue coconut oil at night as well and keep taking the tonic of green and orange water as mentioned above. Strict avoidance should be maintained in diet.

3. *Weakness*
If the diabetic feels weak then he should take cheese, sprouted grains and soup of grams. Red light should be given on the legs and stomach.

Taking the powder of the seed of rose apple along with green water, one teaspoon each in the morning and afternoon will provide strength.

4. High Blood Pressure

For high blood pressure drink green water according to thirst, first thing in the morning. Along with this the patient should take 100-200ml of green water 20-25 minutes before meals and 40-80ml of orange water after the meals. This is a tonic. It should be taken for a long period. At night before sleeping massage 5-6 drops of sun-charged coconut oil on the scalp, temple and forehead for 5-10 minutes slowly using the lower part of the palm. Twice a day inhale sun-charged orange air.

Dry bitter gourd's leaves, seeds, leaves of rose apples, seeds of fenugreek and powder them. Take it twice a day with a teaspoonful of green water. (If the patient cannot make this medicine himself then be can get it form Ashirwad Surya Kiran Chikitsa Aur Rang Chikitsa Kendra) . Now we refer to this *churan* as diabetic *churan*. If one feels weak then one should mix and take one fourth orange water in green water. Fruits and green vegetables should be consumed.

5. Blisters inside the Mouth

Apply sun-charged red oil of sesame seed inside the mouth on the blister. This will make the blister bust open and the dirt will get removed. The application of sun-charged blue coconut oil on the blister will cure the redness and swelling.

6. Low Blood Pressure

For low blood pressure drink green water in the morning before cleaning the bowels, according to thirst and take 100-200ml of green water on an empty stomach before meals and 40-80ml of orange water 8-10 minutes after meals. This is a tonic. It should be taken for a long period. For beneficial results drink an equal mixture of green and orange water along with one tea spoonful of dried and powdered rose apple seeds or leaves. Take the cure regularly for 5-6 weeks.

7. Colour Blindness

On being affected by colour blindness rub sun-charged red oil of sesame seed and take sunlight through red cellophane paper for as long as possible. Do this once or twice a day. Wear red clothes. At night switch on a red bulb. If possible let the colour of the walls of the bedroom also be red and it would be still better if both the bed and bed sheet are also red.

Massage 5-6 drops of sun-charged blue coconut oil on the scalp, temple and forehead slowly using the lower part of the palm for 5-10 minutes. Doing this will provide a sweet and sound sleep. Maintain avoidance in food. Take the soup of black grams 2-3 times a day, reduce the intake of salt. Inhale sun-charged orange air for 5-7 minutes. Do this for 5-6 weeks.

8. *Heart Attack*

Diabetes can also induce heart attack. To prevent the occurrence of a heart attack maintain strict avoidance in diet and do not take fibrous and fried foods, tea, coffee, etc. Only easily digestible food should be taken. Take 100-200ml of green water on an empty stomach 25-30 minutes before the meals and 40-80ml of orange water 8-10 minutes after meals. This is a tonic. It should be taken for a long period.

Diabetes

Name of the disorder	Charged water	Charged medicine	Sunrays	Air	Other remedies
Diabetes without sugar	Green & Brown	Blue coconut oil	–	–	
Diabetes with sugar	Green & Brown	Blue coconut oil	–	–	
Loose motions	Green & Brown	Blue coconut oil	–	–	
Mental tension	Green & Brown	Blue coconut oil	–	–	
Excessive weakness	Green & Brown	Blue coconut oil	–	–	
High blood pressure	Green & Blue	Blue coconut oil	–	–	
Low blood pressure	Green & Blue	Blue coconut oil	–	–	
Blood deficiency	Green & Blue	Blue coconut oil	–	–	
Paralysis	Green & Brown	Red sesame oil	–	–	

Various Other Types of Ailments

> * mental illness * weakness * hiccups * swelling due to serious wound * uprooting of nails * fistula

1. Mental Illness

Mental illness is any disease of the mind that affects a person's thoughts, feelings or behaviour. Most people have periods of sadness, anger and fear. In this ailment for the first week take only green water many times according to thirst. In the second week take 100-200ml of an equal mixture of blue and green water. In the third week one should take the massage of 5-6 drops of sun-charged blue coconut oil on the scalp slowly using the lower part of the palm for 5-10 minutes. Massage it on the forehead and temple also.

Take sunlight through blue cellophane paper at least twice a day for 10-15 minutes. At night the walls of the bed room should be blue, the bulb should also be blue, the bed sheet should be blue. Taking this cure regularly for six months will completely cure the patient and make him normal.

2. Weakness

For weakness drink green water in the morning on an empty stomach. Take 100-200 ml of a mixture of 3 parts of green water and 2 parts of white water thrice a day on an empty stomach 20-25 minutes before meals and drink orange water 10 minutes after meals thrice a day. This will provide strength.

3. Hiccups

On getting hiccups take out the tongue from your mouth and keep it stretched for some time. Suck 10-15 sun-charged red *mishri* thrice a day and massage sun-charged red oil of sesame seed on the hands and neck and drink up to 80ml of the mixture of three parts of orange water and one part of white water.

4. Swelling due to Serious Wound

Apply sun-charged red oil of sesame seed on the swelling and give sunlight through red cellophane paper. Rubbing or massaging sun-charged blue coconut oil on the swelling is beneficial.

5. Uprooting of Nails

Applying sun-charged blue coconut oil on the wound caused will immediately stop the bleeding and its regular application for a few days will cure the wound and the nail will also start growing.

6. Fistula

To cure fistula drink 100-200ml of the mixture of three parts of green water and one part of white water. On the second day there will be fever and acute pain. For acute pain drinking excess of green water 3-4 times a day will make the fistula burst and the pus will come out. After the fistula has burst sun-charged blue coconut oil should be applied on it. Take more of fruits, and green vegetables. Avoid spicy foods. Eat as less as possible so that the stomach is not full. The food taken be easily digestible. For beneficial results drink 40-80ml of orange water after meals.

7

YOGA AND BODY POSTURES

Padamasana (the lotus pose)

The posture of padamasana represents the lotus (*kamal*), hence it is also known as the kamalasana.

Process : Sit down on the floor comfortably. Keep your left leg on your right thigh and right leg on your left thigh in such a way so that the heels touch your belly and both your knees and thighs touch the floor. Keep your back straight. Head, neck, chest and spine should also remain straight and firm. Both your hands should be in the gesture of knowledge (keep your thumb touched to the nails of your index finger and rest of the fingers straight). Now keep your vision fixed on the tip of your nose.

Padamasana

Then sitting as it is in this posture keep both your hands resting on the floor by your side. Now putting pressure on your hands, keep the upper portion of the body firm and sit straight. In the beginning if you can't keep both your legs on your thighs then at least try to sit with one of your leg on your thigh initially. Physically weak or sick persons should not sit in padamasana forcibly, since padamasana is meant for strong and fit persons only. After every third day increase the timings of padamasana by five minutes and gradually reach up to one hour. You can keep your eyes shut, open or half open. Invoke the *muladhar chakra* and imagine that the store of power hidden within the muladhar chakra is opening before you. Concentrate and imagine that an aromatic current is flowing in the heart.

Benefits : The *apan vayu* gets strength in padamasana. The *shushumna* vein remains straight and breathing gets regulated. Padamasana increases enthusiasm. The mind becomes cheerful. The body gets energy. The muscles of the legs become soft, clean and flexible. The mind remains cheerful. Sadness, sorrow and all the problems of the body are vanished. It tones up the abdominal, abdominal organs and the spine.

It is beneficial in impotency. Padamasana acts like a wonder drug in insomnia. This asana helps in relaxation and is a good posture to adopt for meditation.

Sarvangasana (shoulder stand)

Process : Lie on your back. Breathe out and do *rechaka*. Keep the body from the hip to legs straight and together. Loosen your whole body. Lift your legs up slowly. When your legs go up from the floor to thirty degree hold yourself in this position for a little while. Now also raise your hips also. When the legs go up to sixty degree while lifting yourself hold your body in this position for five minutes.

Sarvangasana

Now lift the weight of the legs with the support of your hands on the waist. Rest your elbows on the floor. Let the whole body stand erect putting the weight of the body on the neck and the shoulder. Be careful so that the body comes to a hundred twenty degree angle. The chin should stick to the chest. Keep your eyes fixed on the thumbs of the feet. Now you have to come back to the normal position slowly and holding yourself in the same position taking same time.

Benefits: Practising sarvangasana daily cures stomach problems and increases your appetite. The practitioner should increase his diet as per his requirement and choice. It is also beneficial in hernia,

119

constipation, dyspepsia, heart and throat problems. The heart gets rest by doing this asana which makes the heart strong. It prevents the formation of wrinkles, stops premature greying and hair fall. It increases the energy of the body and purifies the blood. It is also beneficial in diseases of the uterus in women. By doing this asana one can achieve all the benefits of shirshasana. This asana also gives relief in thyroid disease. It controls the fast flow of blood in the body and increases the memory. Pimples and other spots on the face get cured. This asana is beneficial for students.

Asanas Meant for the Vision of the Eyes

First Process : Sit down on the floor. Lift your right arm upto the level of your shoulder. Close your hand into a fist and keep your thumb straight up. Concentrate your vision on the tip of the thumb. Then look at a point eighteen or twenty feet far in some trees, plants or stone without blinking. Continue doing this alternately. Then gently close your eyes. Try to increase the time slowly.

Second Process : Excessive eye work puts strain on them. Get up early in the morning, sit on the bed spreading your legs straight in front of you. Keep your neck and back straight. Then look at a spot measuring the size of a coin six to ten feet away without blinking. Practise this up to five minutes. Vision of the eyes improve by doing this for a long time. Along with this wash your eyes once or twice during the day with solarised water kept in a green bottle to make the eyes healthy.

Asana meant for the vision of the eyes

Third Process : According to Maharishi Patanjali people with defective eyes should keep their eyes fixed on the moon for some time. Moonlight is cool and soothing and helps to cure the eyes. Fix your eyes on the moon and slowly move your head from one side to another. At the same time take your gaze from the moon to the other side. Imagine the moon moving towards the northern side. Look at the moon from different angles. After practising this for two or three days you will find the moon getting more shiny day-by-day and getting close to you. It is a good sign. Fix your eyes on the moon after every five minutes. Close your eyes in between and bat your eyelids after moving your eyes from the moon. After this open your eyes gently. This helps in increasing the vision of the eyes.

Mayurasana (the peacock pose)

Process: Kneel on the floor. Place the feet together and separate the knees. Lean forward and place both palms between the knees on the floor, with the fingers pointing towards the feet. Now keep your palms firmly on the floor. Rest the abdomen on the elbows and chest on the upper arms. Stretch the legs backward so that they are straight and together. The legs and head should be straight in this asana. The whole body should be in a parallel position along the floor. The whole weight of the body should rest on the palm of your hands. Remain in this position for five seconds and come back to the original position. Repeat this once again. Exhale while raising the body off the ground. Inhale while lowering the body. Breathe normally if the final pose is held for a longer period. You can do this asana two to four times.

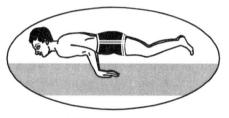

Mayurasana

Benefits : This asana is beneficial in the treatment of stomach ailments, abdominal problems and diabetes. Toxins are eliminated from the blood. This asana is helpful in skin ailments like pimples, acne. It also stimulates the metabolic processes which increase secretion from different organs.

Gorakshasana

The other name of gorakshasana is bhadrasana. To do this asana meditate in *muladhar chakra*, do *puraka* and then do kumbhaka in the second stage.

121

Process : Sit on the floor in siddhasana. Bend both your legs from the knees and clasp your feet in such a way so that both the toes and heels touch each other. Now keep both your hands on the floor and lift your body putting the entire weight on your hands. Then sit on the joints of your heels so that the body weight rests on it. The toes should be free. Now keep both the palms

Gorakshasana

on the knees while doing puraka. Then at the end do kumbhaka and touch the chest with your chin and put pressure on the chest with the chin. Concentrate on the centre of your mind in muladhar chakra and also fix your eyesight there. You can start doing this asana from three minutes and gradually take it up to ten minutes.

Benefits : All the joints, veins and arteries become energetic by doing this asana. The upward movement of the air inside the stomach makes the temperature inside the stomach remain normal. A person becomes active, fit and healthy. Determination increases. The practitioner's intelligence sharpens and he becomes energetic. The digestive system works efficiently, all the food gets digested so one's bowels get cleared properly and one urinates normally. The whole body gets purified. Kundalini gets invoked and enters the *shushumna* vein. This asana makes the legs and feet extremely flexible.

This asana prevents loss of semen, cures flatuleuce, diabetes, indigestion, hip pain, constipation, dyspepsia, headache, tuberculosis, heart diseases, insomnia, asthma, epilepsy, piles, appendix, jaundice, dropsy, anal fistula, leprosy, vomiting, hiccups eye problems etc.

Pawan Muktasana (the wind liberating posture)

This *pawan muktasana* helps the body to breathe out all the air from the stomach to the heart. This is why this asana is known as the *pawan muktasana.* This asana can be done in two ways.

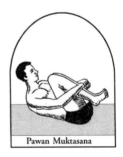

Pawan Muktasana

1. First Process : Lie down on your back on the floor. Keep both your legs straight. Fold your legs up to the chest. Put your arms around the knees and interlock your fingers. Do *purak* and breathe in. Now bend your right leg and bring it up to your chest and hold it tightly along with the stomach. Be careful to keep your other leg straight. Then lift your head up and touch your knees with the nose. Hold your breath and do *kumbhaka* while doing this process. After doing this make your right leg straight. Once this is done keep your head and the folded leg properly on the floor and only then do *rechaka*. Repeat the procedure with the other leg also. This asana can also be done by folding both the legs together.

2. Second Process : Raise your head while breathing in but breathe out while bending your knees. Hold your breath as far as possible. Come back to the original position while breathing in. This asana should not be done more than two to four minutes.

Benefits : This asana helps to reduce the fat in your stomach. It cures constipation, flatulence and relieves the stomach of all the problems. If you are suffering from indigestion then you will be benefited from this asana. If your bowels are not cleared properly in the morning then do this asana ten to twenty minutes after drinking water. If you roll yourself forward and backward while doing this asana you will be benefited. This asana increases memory. Intellectuals, students, those who sit and work throughout the day, should do this asana regularly.

Shirshasana (the headstand pose)

Shirsha means 'head'. In this asana the practitioner has to stand upside down on his head. That's why it is called *shirshasana*.

Shirshasana

Process : Sit in vajrasana. Bend forward and place the forearms on the ground with fingers intertwined. Place the crown of the head between the intertwined hands. Lift the knees off the ground and raise the buttocks until the legs are straight. Slowly transfer the body weight from the toes onto the head and arms and raise one foot a few inches off the ground. Raise the other foot and balance on the head and arms. The body should be perfectly straight in the final pose.

Benefits: This asana increases the blood flow to the brain, removes psychological disturbances and relieves headaches, asthma, hay fever, etc. It is the greatest of all asanas as it totally revitalises the mind and body.

Vajrasana (thunderbolt pose)

Vajra means stone, strong or energetic. This asana makes the body strong like a *vajra* and that's why it is called *vajrasana*.

You have to meditate in muladhar chakra in this asana and be careful in breathing.

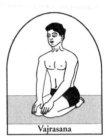
Vajrasana

Process : Stand on the knees with feet stretched backward and toes crossed. The knees should be together and heels apart. Lower the buttocks onto the insides of the feet, the heels at the sides of the hips. Place the hands on the knees, palms downward.

Benefits : This vajrasana is the only asana which can be done after meals. The digestive system works efficiently if a person sits in this asana after taking meals. You can do vajrasana for twenty seconds initially and gradually increase it to half an hour. Vajrasana improves the eyesight. *Vajra nari* (the sperm flowing vein) becomes strong. This *asana* stops the restlessness of the mind and makes it peaceful and steady. It cures the impurities in the flow of blood and makes the body fit, free from diseases and beautiful. It gives relief from constipation and cures all stomach diseases. It also gives relief in jaundice. It cures the rheumatic problems of the hips and legs. It cures the irregularities of menses among women. Semen disorders, sperm disorders, knee pain, etc., also get cured by this asana. This asana is also good for meditating. Day-by-day it increases energy in the body. Hence the body becomes energetic.

Naoli Kriya

Process : By bending the shoulder forward, and moving the intestines of the stomach fast in a round movement is called naoli kriya. Stand with your legs one to one and a half feet apart to do *naoli kriya*. Bend the knees a little and keep both your hands on your thighs in such a way so that the fingers are directed inwards. Your eyes should be fixed on your stomach, now breathe out all the air from your lungs through the nostrils and do *uddiyan bandh.* Pull the muscles of the stomach inwardly. Pull the intestines and naval of the stomach inside. Then leave the right and left side and loosen the middle portion. So that the muscles can be seen from the above in the form of tubes.

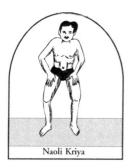

Naoli Kriya

This is known as *madhya naoli* (middle naoli). In the same we can squeeze the right and left side and do *dakshin naoli* (south naoli) and by loosening the left side do *baye naoli* (left *naoli*). This naoli kriya should be done after clearing the bowels and before taking meals.

Benefits : This is a very good exercise for the stomach. It clears the bowels properly. Constipation gets cured and the stomach starts functioning well. Naoli kriya influences indigestion and gives relief. Naoli kriya cures rheumatism, biles, cough, etc., and other diseases. Naoli kriya is the best kriya of *hato yog.*

Advices : Naoli kriya should be done peacefully. Naoli kriya should not be done if there is any problem with the intestines or if you are suffering from bile, diarrhoea, stomachache and chronic disorders of the bowels.

Ashwasana (the horse pose)

Ashwa means horse. After finishing the whole day's work a horse lies down with both its legs on one side and the neck on the other side. In this way a horse relieves himself of his tiredness within a few minutes and once again becomes fresh

Ashwasana

and ready to work. That's why this is known as ashwasana.

Process : Lie down on your back. Bend both your legs from the knees and take them to one side. Spread both your hands parallel to your shoulders. Keep your fists closed and breathe in. Keep your stomach filled with air and hold your breath under the naval. Just as you squeeze your towel similarly squeeze yourself in the same way and come back to the normal position while breathing out. Now repeat the procedure by turning to the other side. After doing this procedure on both sides one cycle is completed. In this way this can be done from one cycle to twenty-five to fifty cycles. If you are suffering from constipation then always drink chilled or lukewarm water before doing this asana. This asana helps in the normal bowel functioning.

Benefits : This is like a life-saving wonder herb for the city dwellers. Foam mattresses are used in maximum homes. Many diseases related to neck and spinal cord are increasing day-by-day. This asana can cure these diseases totally. If this asana is done when a person feels lazy and tired, it will make him cheerful and energetic.

If this asana is done before retiring to bed it will help the person to get a sound sleep. If this asana is done regularly it will help the displaced naval to come back to its position. It works miraculously in hip pain, pain in the spine and stiffness. If your hip bone is bending down then this asana will help the hip bone to straighten up automatically. This asana is beneficial for health and beauty. It influences the stomach and intestines and cures constipation. It should be done five to ten minutes daily.

Halasana (the plough pose)

Hal means plough. The body takes the form of a plough in halasana. That's why it is known as halasana. To do this asana you have to meditate in *vishuddhi* chakra and do breathing in *rechaka* and *bandha*.

Process : Lie down on the floor on your back. Keep both your hands straight by your side. Breathe out while keeping both your legs together. Take both your legs up together and then to the backside of the head so that the tip of your toes touch the floor. By doing this your hips and back will come above your head. Keep both your legs straight and firm. Touch the chest with your chin properly. In this way your chin will get fixed to the cavity of your throat. In the final position both your hands will be on the other side of your head and the fingers will be together resting on the floor. Be steady and meditate on *chitta vishuddhi chakra.*

Halasana

You can do this asana starting from three minutes and gradually increase it up to twenty minutes. Then for coming back to the first position keep your hands at the same place. The way the legs were raised up in the same way they should be brought down.

Benefits: This asana relieves constipation and removes fat from the waist. It helps to cure diabetes, piles and tones the spinal nerves.

Shalabhasana (the locust pose)

Shalabh means locust. In this asana the posture of the body becomes like a locust. That's why this asana is known as *shalabhasana*.

Shalabhasana

Process : Lie down straight upwards down on your stomach on the floor and keep both the legs touching the floor together. The chin should be kept resting on the floor. Now close your fist tightly and gradually lift both the legs together as far as possible by the force of the hands. Be careful so that the knees don't bend. They should be kept absolutely straight. Now lift one of the legs with the force of your hand as high as possible and hold it there for sometime. When you start to breathe out repeat the previous process gently. Then bring it back to the floor with force. This asana can be done twice or thrice at a time. When this asana is done with one leg it is called ardha shalabhasana.

Benefits : It is beneficial for the thighs, stomach, arms, etc. The intestines of the stomach become stronger. It expands the chest and makes the lower portion of the spine flexible. All stomach problems and constipation gets cured. This asana is specially beneficial in hernia and diabetes. It prevents the naval from being dislocated.

Utthanpadasana

Utthan means lifting up and *pad* means legs. Lie down on your back and lift it a little and stretch it. This is why it is called *utthanpadasana*.

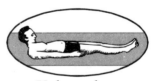

Utthanpadasana

Process : Lie down on your back on the floor, lift your legs a little and stretch it. The knees, heels and the fingers of the feet will touch each

127

other. After that spread both your hands on your side touching the legs below the hips and lift your neck, chest and legs, one foot from the floor keeping both your hands straight. Then raise your head a little, look at your toes. According to your ability breathe in and hold your breath. At the end breathe out and rest your legs gradually on the floor. You should do this asana by counting from two to five.

Benefits : This asana cures the dislocation of the naval. It leaves a good effect on the total naval region, where the centre of seventy-two thousand veins is situated. It cures constipation, all stomach problems and reduces the fat from the stomach and the buttocks.

Ardha Matsendrasana

There lived a great yogi by the name of Matsendra. He used to meditate in this asana. That's why this asana is known as *matsendrasana*. It has been simplified.

Process : Bend the right leg to the left and place the left heel against the right buttock. Place the left arm outside the left leg and with the left hand hold the right foot or ankle. The right knee should be as near as possible to the left armpit. Turn the body to the right, placing the right arm behind the back. Twist the back and then the neck as far as possible.

Ardh Matsendrasana

Benefits : This ardha matsendrasana keeps the spine healthy which makes the life youthful. It tones the spinal nerves, makes the back muscles supple and loosens the vertebrae. The different parts of the stomach get benefited by this asana. It cures constipation and increases the appetite. All the diseases of the intestines and heart and spleen problems are cured. It also cures hip pains, backache, joint pain very easily and improves the health. This asana activates the pancreas and is therefore useful in eliminating diabetes.

Dhanurakarshanasana (the archer's pose)

You have to meditate in *manipur chakra* in this asana. Breathe in the lower side and do *rechaka*, breathe in the higher side and do *puraka*.

128

Process : Sit with legs stretched forward. Place the left foot on the right thigh and grasp the right toe from the top with the left hand. Hold the left toe with the right hand, keeping the right leg straight. The left toe should touch the right ear. Do not bend the neck or back. Inhale while seated prior to pulling toe to the ear. Retain inside while pulling the toe. Exhale on returning to the half lotus pose.

Dhanurasan

Benefits : This asana cures all stomach ailments, constipation, etc., and increases appetite. Even the weakest and feeble persons can do this asana and reap benefits from it. The benefit of this asana is equal to the benefit of a combination of mayurasana, shalabhasana and bhujungasana together. This asana helps to reduce the fat from the stomach and gives relief in gastric problems. It gives relief in chest pain and makes the heart stronger. Breathing becomes normal. This asana also tones the abdominal organs, and stretches the spine. It improves the vision of the eyes curing all eye diseases.

According to Maharshi Patanjali this asana is beneficial for females. It cures all menstrual problems and other diseases of the uterus.

Supta Vajrasana (the horizontal hardy pose)

You have to meditate in vishuddhi chakra, take deep breath and lie down in vajrasana to do supta vajrasana.

Process : Sit down in vajrasana and then lie down on your back. Both the thighs should be kept with one another. Now while doing *rechak* raise your hands and keep them under your head. After completing *rechaka* do all the three *bandhs*. Keep your eyesight fixed and mind centered on the *muladhar chakra*.

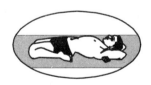

Supta Vajrasana

Benefits : This asana is easy to do and very beneficial. This asana makes the path of *shushumna* vein smooth. The *kundalini shakti* goes upward and invokes the mind easily. This asana is beneficial in hip pain, knee pain, throat problems, cervical, gout, menstrual problem, etc. Supta vajrasana cures humps. The spinal cord becomes flexible and strong like a vajra. All the glands like glands of the brain, glands of the throat, urinal glands, glands of the male reproductive organ, etc. become strong. It helps in the development of people physically and religiously. It makes the mind and body healthy. It increases appetite, cures constipation, paralysis, forming of stone in any part of the body, stammering, all diseases of the throat, swelling of the respiratory pipe, tuberculosis, asthma and improves eyesight and weak memory.

Shavasana (the corpse pose)

Shava means dead body. The body becomes like a corpse. The body part gets relaxed in this asana. That's why this asana is known as shavasana.

Process : Lie flat on your back on the floor in a relaxed position. Spread your legs apart, so that there is a distance of 18 to 20 inches between them. Heels should be inside and toes pointing

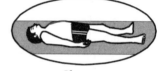

Shavasana

outwards. Spread your hands by your side so that the palm of your hands face the sky. Close your eyes and let all the parts of the body relax. Breathe gently and observe your breath by concentrating on it. Shift your attention to your toes, and concentrate on your feet. In this manner, observe each part of your body. You will experience total relaxation.

If shavasana is done according to proper rules, the practitioner will feel sleepy. But it is essential to remain awake even after falling asleep. Shavasana should be done according to the ability of the practitioner. If you are suffering from insomnia then do this asana before retiring to bed. This asana will make you fall asleep. You can do this asana two to three times whenever you have time.

Benefits : It gives comfort and energy to the whole body. You can get rid of tiredness. With continuous practice of this asana, one can achieve a state of total relaxation. Patients suffering from heart diseases and high blood pressure can be benefitted by doing this asana for ten minutes in the morning and evening regularly.

Bhujangasana or Sarpasana (the cobra pose)

Process : Lie face down, with your forehead touching the ground, feet and toes parallel to the ground and hands at your sides. Lift the upper part of your body and balance the body weight on your palrns – as shown in the figure. Slowly raise the head and shoulders from the

Bhujangasana

ground, bending the head as far back without strain. Remain in their position as long as you are confortable. This restores your youth and vitality.

Benefits : It stimulates the appetite and eliminates constipation. This asana is beneficial for all abdominal organs, especially the liver and kidneys. It relocates slipped discs, removes backache and keeps the spine supple and healthy.

Chakrasana (the wheel pose)

Process: Lie on your back on the floor. Bend your knees and heels touching the buttocks. The feet should be one foot apart. Place the palms on the ground beside the temples. Slowly raise the trunk. Straighten the arms and legs, lift the head and raise the body to its fully arched height. Slowly lower yourself back to the ground.

Chakrasana

Make your mind centered at the *manipur chakra* which is also known as the naval centre. You can keep your eyes open while doing this asana. You can start doing this asana from 30 seconds and gradually increase it to four minutes.

Benefits : This asana is very good for women. It makes the body light and fresh. The veins of the body get purified. This asana invokes the yogic chakra also. It cures paralysis and fatigue. It prevents the tummy from becoming loose.

It increases the height and makes the body healthy and beautiful. Hip pain, dislocation of the naval get cured and the spinal cord

131

becomes flexible. It makes all the body parts strong and energetic. It increases the digestive power and removes unwanted fat from the stomach. It keeps the body straight and erect. This asana is actually a substitute for paschimottanasana.

Gomukhasana (the cow face pose)

The posture of the body in this asana resembles the face of the cow, hence it is known as *gomukhasana*.

Process : Sit in siddhasana. Bend your left leg and keep it against the right buttock. Bend the right leg to the left. One knee should be kept on another knee. Lift the right hand and take it to the backside towards the hips. Now take the other hand back and keep it bent firmly. Now clasp the fingers of the upper hand with the lower hand tightly. In the same way do it with the other side. You can do this procedure from one to five minutes. Breathe normally while practising this asana.

Gomukhasana

Benefits : This gomukhasana is beneficial for lungs. It is specially beneficial for asthma. It cures diabetes, frequent urinating, backache and pain in the neck. This asana makes the hands and fingers strong and supple. It is also helpful in hernia.

Gardan (Neck) Tiryag Akarshanasana

This gardan (neck) tiryag akarshanasana is divided into four parts. This is a simple asana and gives lot of benefits.

First process : Sit on the floor in vajrasana with your back and neck stretched. Then keep both the hands on your knees. Stretch your spine and make your neck loose, bend forward and try to touch the chin with your chest. In the same way try to bend backwards to touch the back with the back portion of your head. Try to do this asana in as much simple ways as

Neck Tiryag Akarshanasana

possible. But don't force yourself. You can do this asana for five to ten times at a time.

Second process : Sit down in vajrasana on the floor and keep the hands on the knees. Stretch your neck and back and sit straight. Then stretch the spine and loosen your neck. After this, move the neck gently first to the backside and then to the front downwards. Then rotate the neck softly like a grinding stone used in the olden days for grinding. In the same way first move the neck from the right side and gently rotate it. You can rotate it like this for five to ten times at a time. Then again start rotating it from the other side. You can again do this for five to ten times at a time.

Neck Tiryag
Akarshansana

Benefits : This asana removes the stiffness of the neck and makes it flexible. This asana is beneficial in thyroid and cures tonsils. If you have problem in moving your neck from one side to another then it will get cured by this asana.

Vrischikasana

Lie down on your chest and rest both your arms from elbows to the palms on the floor. Then bend your legs from knees backwards and keep your feet on your head.

Benefits : This asana increases the strength of your hands and arms. It makes the body light and cheerful.

Vrischikasana

Paschimottanasana (the back stretching pose)

This asana is a bit hard. Lord Shiva himself has said that this asana is one of the best asana. In paschimottanasana, *paschim* means back portion, *utthan* means stretching. That's why this asana is called *paschimottanasana*. Maharshi Patanjali has advised to keep this asana a secret. Only instructors should explain the mystery.

Process: Lie down on your back on the floor. Now take your hands to the back of your head. Spread your legs straight in front of you. Keep both your legs, thigh, knees together touching each other and your body touching the floor. Now without any help and without giving a jerk to the body lift the upper portion of your body gradually along with your hands spread forward. Bend yourself forward towards your legs. Try to hold the toes with your fingers. Now do *rechak* and again bend forward. Slowly bend your head and keep it in the middle of your knees.

Paschimotthanasana

Be careful while bending forward to hold the toes. Let both your elbows touch the floor beside the knees. After completing the *rechaka* do *kumbhaka*. Hold yourself for two to four seconds, then leave your toes and lie down on your back as before. Now concentrate on *manipur chakra*. It should be done slowly. You can repeat this three to four times. But you can do this asana from three seconds to fifteen seconds only. During the first two to four days you will find it difficult to do this but gradually it will become easy.

Benefits : This asana makes all the muscles of the body specially the muscles of the back and heart firm. It reduces the increased heart beat and makes it normal. Doing this asana regularly will open the end of the *shushumna* vein (*kundalini*). It also cures constipation, joint pain, diabetes and is beneficial in uterus problems in women. It also activates the kidneys, liver, pancreas and adrenal glands.

Women who are suffering from sexual disorders should do this asana. This asana prevents accumulation of fats in the body. It also helps to get rid of worms. This asana is good for people with a bulging belly. Physical and mental tensions are cured. All the oxygen of the body starts functioning properly.

This asana cures cold, cough, all sorts of rheumatism, hip pain, blood disorders, appendicitis, hiccups, leprosy, urine problem, diseases of the legs, nocturnal pollution, jaundice, sleep, sour belches, swelling of the naval, irregular periods in women, painful menses, barrenness, leucorrhoea, impotency, dwarfness, etc. It makes the digestive system more efficient and reduces the fats of the body. It helps to tone the abdominal region.

This asana helps to increase the height to a great extent and is a very powerful asana for spiritual awakening.

It is the main asana among all the asanas. It brings dramatic changes in our body. This is the most favourite asana of Lord Shiva. Yogi Gorakhnath propagated this asana as per the order of Lord Shiva for the betterment of this world.

Janushirasana

Process : Sit down on the floor. Now spread your right leg forward and bend the left leg against the right buttock. Pull the fingers of the right foot with both the hands and gradually bend your face forward and rest your forehead on

Janushirasana

the knees of the right leg. When this procedure is complete on one side spread your left leg and by bending the right leg follow the same procedure. You can repeat this asana two to four times.

Benefits : All the benefits of this asana are similar to paschimottanasana. The speciality of this asana is that, the sperm disorders are cured. This asana is very helpful to invoke the *kundalini*. For practical benefits this asana should be done for ten minutes only.

Dwihasta Chakrasana

Process: Stand on the floor with your feet twenty inches apart. Stretch your body and slowly get the hands stretched in front parallel to your shoulders and stand. Now while breathing in slowly take the hands up by stretching them and stretch them as far as possible like tarasana. Then while breathing out stretch the hands in front of

Dwihasta Chakrasana

135

you keeping them parallel to your shoulder. Then slowly turn your whole body to the right. Your feet should be kept firmly in the same place. Turn your body so much so that your hands go towards the back and also turn your face from the right to the top of your shoulder. Then bring your body back to the position. Slowly bring down the stretched hands and take rest. After taking rest again stretch your body and repeat the same procedure on the left side. You can do this asana for three to six times at a time.

Benefits : This asana makes the shoulders strong and flexible and cures any pain in them. Rheumatic problems are prevented and cured by doing this asana. It expands the chest and makes it strong.

Advice : It should be kept in mind that while doing this asana the whole body should be kept stretched and the hands should be stretched with full effort like tarasana.

Ushtrasana (the camel pose)

Ushtra means camel. In this asana, the posture looks like camel's neck. So this is called *ushtrasana.*

Process : Sit down in vajrasana. Breathe in and bend backwards. Bend your neck and try to hold your feet with your hands. Arch as far back as possible. Return to the kneeling position, then back to vajrasana. You can do this asana from fifteen seconds to three minutes.

Ushtrasana

Benefits : This asana is beneficial in hip pain, diseases of the chest, lungs and heart, etc. It reduces the fat from the stomach, makes the digestive system strong and the spinal cord flexible. It cures jaundice, eye problems and nourishes all the parts of the body.

Naukasana (the boat pose)

The posture of the body in this asana becomes like that of a boat. Hence it is called naukasana.

Process : Lie on your stomach to do this asana and spread both your hands forward

Naukasana

and fold them. Then while pulling the upper portion of the stomach and the lower portion of the stomach on either side lift the front part of the body and back portion of the body so that the whole body, the legs and hands come in the posture of a boat. Now swing the body in the front and back like a boat. This is the way a boat floats in the water and gets jerks. This asana can be done two to four times in this way.

Benefits : This asana is very good for relaxing the muscles and joints. It reduces the fats from the stomach. It is beneficial in constipation and any disease of the lungs. It makes the digestive system stronger. It also helps in reducing tension and brings immediate relaxation.

8

PRANAYAMA AND APANAYAMA

Murchapranayama (the fainting pranayama)

In this pranayama the total energy of the mind is due to *kumbhaka*. Breath controls the *pran*. The regulation of the *pran* wins over the mind. The *pran* starts staying in the condition of *kumbhaka*.

Process : Sit down on the floor in padamasana. Keep the neck and spine straight. Close the eyes gently. Keep your thumbs on both the ears, index fingers gently on the eyes, middle fingers on the nostrils and both the ring fingers on your lips. Lift the fingers from the nostrils a little and breathe in lightly. Then close the nostrils and do *kumbhaka* internally. Increase the timings while doing *kumbhaka*, which is beneficial in this pranayama. When you are unable to hold your breath anymore

Murchapranayama

lift the finger from the nostril gently and open the *jallandhar bandha*. Breathe out gently. Repeat this procedure three to five times. You can increase it with your full energy.

Benefits : It induces tranquillity in the whole body and mind and provides relaxation. It is beneficial for people who suffer from mental problems. It is an excellent preparation for meditation.

Agnisarpranayama

This pranayama increases the appetite so it is called *Agnisar pranayama*. It is very essential to make the digestive system stronger.

Agnisar Pranayama

Process : It can be done by sitting in padamasana or siddhasana or it can also be done while standing or lying down. This pranayama is beneficial to keep the digestive system healthy. Now breathe out and do *uddiyan bandh*. Repeat this at least thrice. You can move the stomach in and out with your full strength 15 to 20 times.

Benefits : The main benefit of this pranayama is that it reduces the fats of the stomach and cures constipation.

Shitli Pranayama (the cooling breath)

By practising this *shitli pranayama* the body gets cooled. Our hermits and sages knew the art of keeping the body cool in the hot season. It is one of the most important pranayamas done during summer season. It cools the nerves and veins of the body. This is why it is known as shitli pranayama. It helps to maintain water balance in the body.

Process : Sit down in padamasana or siddhasana and lift the chin one or two inches high. Keep your spine straight and bring out your tongue and fold the sides to form a narrow tube. Now pull the air through the tongue in the piped position and gently fill the lungs with air. Then close your mouth and hold your breath for sometime and breathe out through your nostril. This pranayama should be done five times daily. It can be increased to ten times.

Benefits : It eliminates thirst and purifies the blood. This pranayama should be done during summer, since it provides comfort and coolness. It cures biles, acidity, high blood pressure and skin diseases. It is also beneficial in fever. It controls insomnia. It makes the body energetic, healthy and beautiful.

Surya Bhedi Pranayama (the vitality stimulating technique)

Surya bhedi pranayama makes all the veins energetic. It gives the heat equal to that of sun. In this pranayama *puraka* is done again and again through the right nostril. The surya vein is invoked, hence it is known as surya bhedi pranayama. This pranayama should be done in winter.

Process : To do the surya bhedi pranayama sit down in siddhasana or padamasana and close the left nostril with the help of the little finger and ring finger of the right hand. Breathe in as much as you can through the right nostril and do *kumbhaka* for some time. Then press

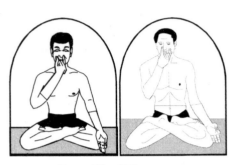

Surya Bhedi Pranayama

the right nostril with the thumb and do *kumbhaka* as much as you can starting from five times initially and do it up to twenty times. Do this gently and increase the time of *kumbhaka* gradually. It influences the *shat chakra.*

Benefits : This asana generates heat in the body and energises the digestive system. Cold, cough, asthma, rheumatic problems, headaches and vocal disorders like stammering are also cured by it. It is very beneficial in diabetes.

Advice : Heart patients should not do this pranayama. People suffering from asthma should not do *kumbhaka* in this pranayama.

Shitkari Pranayama (the hissing breath)

In this shitkari pranayama a shi-shi sound comes out. Creating this sound makes the body cool. Bad breath goes away. It is very helpful in diseases like pyorrhoea. That is why it is called shitkari pranayama.

Shitkari Pranayama

Process : Sit down in siddhasana or padamasana. Keep your tongue touched to the upper wall of your mouth. Keep the upper and lower teeth on one another, create the shi-shi sound and do *puraka.* Try to do *kumbhaka* as much as possible and gently do *rechaka* with both the nostrils. In this way you can start by counting ten and gradually increase it to counting fifty daily. You can do this pranayama while standing and also while moving around. You can also do this by keeping the tongue in between the teeth.

Benefits : This pranayama makes the body cool. It quenches thirst and increases appetite. It also destroys poison in the body, cools the bile, cures diseases of the teeth, fever and fatigue.

Advice : Patients suffering from cold and cough, breathing problems should not do shitkari pranayama.

Chandra Bhedi Pranayama

If you do the opposite of surya bhedi pranayama you will accomplish doing *chandra bhedi pranayama*.

Since this pranayama influences the *swar* (*chandra* veins) flowing by the left nose, therefore it is known as the chandra bhedi pranayama. This pranayama cools the body.

Process : Sit down in padamasana or sukhasana and close the right nostril with the thumb of the right hand. In this pranayama *purak* is done by the left nostril (*chandra swar*) again and again which invokes the *chandra* veins. Hence it is known as the chandra bhedi pranayama.

Benefits : This pranayama relieves tiredness and makes the body cool. It is beneficial in high blood pressure, gives mental peace and infuses the body with nector. This pranayama is very useful to cool the heat of the body. It also cures many skin diseases. This pranayama should

Chandra Bhedi Pranayama

not be done in winter. Do this pranayama only in summer. People suffering from asthma, heart problems, high blood pressure should do this pranayama. This asana should be done in very hot season.

Apanayama

Just as health can be improved by perfecting the *prana vayu* (breath) with the help of pranayama, in the same way we can perfect and control *apan vayu* with the help of apanayama and become healthy.

The pranayama controls the portion from the throat to the heart. And the apan vayu controls the portion from the naval to the anus. Many diseases take place sometimes causing death also due to any disturbance of the *apan vayu*. Apan vayu makes the body clean, fresh and free from any ailments.

Constipation, headache and all sorts of stomach problems are due to the failure of *apan vayu* and the process used to purify the apan vayu is known as apanayama.

First Process : Inflate your stomach in the front as much as you can, then squeeze it inwards. Try to pull the naval internally to touch the spine. It purifies the *apan vayu*. Now keep both the hands on your stomach in such a way so that the thumbs are kept on the back and the other fingers are in the front. Now inflate your stomach as previously done and press on the right side with your left hand. Then press with your right hand on the back side. Now inflate stomach left and right from the back. After

Breathing in

doing it for a few days the stomach will automatically move from the left to the right and go to the back and again to the left on its own. This cleans the stomach and the apana vayu is perfected and controlled.

Second process : Stand straight and breathe out totally and try to pull both the sides of the chest internally as far as possible. Keep the naval above. Take a table or something that can be held or lifted while doing this. Now lift it with your hands and hold it. The naval will come out on its own. Now remove your hand from the table and keep it on your knees and breathe out. Then pull the stomach internally till the naval comes out. Now you can hold the breath while breathing in and out. This process perfects the apan vayu and cures many stomach disorders.

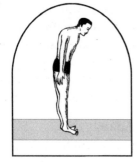

Third process : We must have
seen dogs and cats stretching
themselves. Position yourself in
the same way. Stretch your hands
in the front. Let your chin and
cheeks touch the floor. Keep

your knees apart. Try to bend your hips forward as far as possible.
Now try to breathe out. Then automatically you will breathe in.

Benefits : Flatulence and headache get cured by this process. Only
puraka and *rechaka* should be done in apanayama, you should not do
kumbhaka. Loosen your stomach as far as possible then all the air will
come out automatically.

9
SURYA NAMASKAR

First Step : Fold your hands and stand with your heels together and toes and fingers kept apart. Keep your head, neck and body straight. Breathe normally.

"Om Mitraye Namah"

First Step

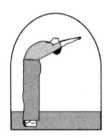

Second Step

Second Step : Stretch your hand above and bend to your back while breathing in and hold your breath in for a while. (Do *kumbhaka*).

"Om Ravey Namah"

Third Step : Now bend forward so that your hands rest on the floor and let your head touch your knees while breathing out. Keep your knees straight. (Do *kumbhaka*)

"Om Suryay Namah"

Third Step

Fourth Step : Take your left leg backwards but don't bend your arms or elbows. Lift your face up towards the sky and keep your hips down while breathing in (Try to do *kumbhaka* also)

"Om Bhanvey Namah"

Fourth Step

Fifth Step

Fifth Step : Take both your legs backwards let both your toes and heels touch each other while breathing out. Touch your throat with the chin. Keep your buttocks and the back of your head in a straight line. (Do *Kumbhaka*)

"Om Khragay Namah"

Sixth Step : In this step you have to first breathe in and lie down on your chest on the floor so that your legs, knees, chest, chin, nose and the forehead touch the floor. Then breathe out. Keep the elbows upwards and raise the stomach from the floor.

"Om Pushney Namah"

Sixth Step

Seventh Step

Seventh Step : While breathing in keep your hand and arms straight and position your head like bhujangasana.

"Om Hiranyagarvay Namah"

Eighth Step : In this step you come back to the position given in step five and look inwards and outwards while breathing out.

"Om Marichay Namah"

Eighth Step

Ninth Step : While breathing in take your left leg between your arms and go back to the position given in step four.

"Om Aditaya Namah"

Ninth Step

Tenth Step

Tenth Step : While breathing out go back to the position given in step three.

"Om Sabitray Namah"

Eleventh Step : While breathing in go back to the position given in step two.

"Om Arkaya Namah"

Eleventh Step

Twelfth Step

Twelfth Step : While breathing out go back to the position given in step one.

(This is a full round of Surya Namaskar)

"Om Bhaskaray Namah"

Benefits of Surya Namaskar

1. Patients with breathing problems benefit by the regularised procedure of breathing in and breathing out. Constipation, piles and breathing problems are cured.

2. It stimulates and tones up all the nerve centres and energises the energy centres of the body.

3. Surya Namaskar accompanied by asanas energise the central nervous system.

4. Regular practice helps you to achieve good health and a greater balance of mind.

5. The mental peace and intelligence of the practitioner increases. It helps to increase memory.

6. It is the best scientific way of exercise to increase flexibility.

Introduce Laughter in Your Life

It's not wrong to say that the cheerfulness of our mind depends totally on ourselves. When we try to be cheerful we certainly become cheerful. And if we consider ourselves sad we remain sad and disappointed. Your thoughts influence your feelings, emotions and your health. So you should always remain cheerful.

1. It is essential for children to go on giggling to keep themselves energetic and fit.

2. If the teacher with whom a child spends most of his time is angry and rude the child will become a introvert and unfit.

3. Laughing makes the muscles of the stomach function efficiently. This increases the digestive power and the efficiency of the blood vessels. It also increases your appetite.

4. It is a pleasant exercise. Laughing brings many facial muscles in to play and diffuses stress.

5. People who laugh a lot seldom suffer from lung diseases as the lungs are filled up with fresh air everytime one laughs.

6. Laughter is an infallible medicine.

7. Laughter cures many diseases like chronic constipation, tuberculosis, etc.

10

HAST MUDRAS

The Gesture of the Sun

This gesture of the sun is done by touching the root of the thumb with the ring finger and pressing the ring finger with the thumb.

Benefits : This gesture is very beneficial for our body. It helps keeping the balance of the body and reduces weight and cholesterol in the body. It also cures diabetes, and diseases of the heart, kidney, spleen etc.

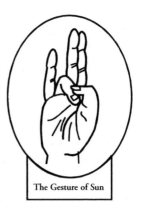

The Gesture of Sun

The Gesture of Apana

Touch the tip of the thumb by bending the middle and ring finger together.

Benefits : It purifies the veins of the body, cures constipation, gives relief in gastric pain, clears the bowels, cures piles, relieves urinal problems, cures diabetes, dental problems, etc. It is beneficial in all stomach problems. It is good for the heart. But this gesture makes a person sweat and urinate more.

The Gesture of Apana

The Gesture of Knowledge

This gesture is a combination of the thumb and the index finger.

Benefits : It increases memory and knowledge, helps develop interest in studies, cures headache, helps to get rid of anger, cures mental tension, irritation and insomnia. This gesture of knowledge is a boon for students and intellectuals.

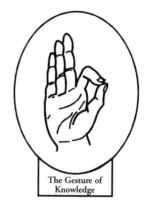

The Gesture of
Knowledge

The Gesture of Air

The gesture of air is done by touching the index finger to the root of the finger and pressing the index finger in this position with the thumb.

Benefits : It helps to cure all sorts of gastric problems, joint pains, paralysis, body pain, diseases of the neck and spine, knee pain, pain of the spinal cord, etc.

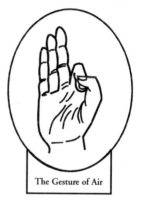

The Gesture of Air

The Gesture of Varuna

Bend the little finger to touch the tip of the thumb.

Benefits : This gesture can cure any disease arising due to dearth of water element. It cures skin diseases, pimples and makes the body healthy and beautiful. It also cures all skin diseases and blood problems.

Advice : A person who is suffering from severe cold and cough problems should not practise this gesture too much.

The Gesture
of Varuna

The Gesture of the Earth

This gesture can be done by touching the tip of the thumb with the tip of the ring finger.

Benefits : It makes the body energetic. The health improves, a thin person becomes healthy, gains weight. This gesture makes the person well disposed and increases memory and stamina. It also increases the energy of the brain.

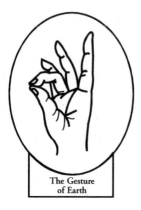

The Gesture
of Earth

The Gesture of Apanvayu or Heart

Touch the palm of your hand by bending the index finger or touch the root of the thumb. Now touch the middle and ring finger with the thumb. It is essential to keep the little finger straight in this gesture.

Benefits : This gesture prevents heart attacks and is equivalent to an injection. A weak heart can be cured by regular practise of this gesture. It gives relief from flatulence. It is beneficial in headache and asthma. Heart patients and patients suffering from high blood pressure should do this gesture five minutes before climbing the stairs.

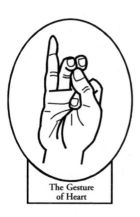

The Gesture
of Heart